CHANSONS DES QUATRE SAISONS

Réalisation du disque

Enregistré et mixé chez Audio Z en septembre 2008
Réalisation, arrangements, casting et direction musicale : Patrice Dubuc
Collaboration aux arrangements vocaux : Vincent Morel
Mixage des chansons, prise de son des poèmes et mastering : Luc Thériault
Sonorisation des poèmes : Alexandre Wang-Legentil
Prise de son des voix, violon et accordéon : Alexandre Wang-Legentil
Prise de son des autres instruments : Patrice Dubuc au studio Lady Trenton.

Musiciens

Guitares acoustiques, classiques et électriques, basse électrique, mandoline, banjo,
yukulele, harmonica et claviers : Patrice Dubuc
Flûte traversière : Luc Thériault
Basson : Danielle Hébert
Accordéon diatonique et percussions « aux os » : Sabin Jacques
Claviers et collaboration aux arrangements orchestraux : Gaëtan Gravel
Violon : André Proulx

Interprètes

Chanteurs : Julie Leblanc, Catherine Léveillé, Vincent Morel et José Paradis
Narrateur des poèmes : Alexis Lefebvre

Patrice Dubuc tient à remercier Suzanne Dubuc pour ses bons conseils, Serge Laforest et
Audio Z, Eric Thexton qui lui a prêté sa superbe mandoline ainsi que Stéphanie et Marion.

Ce disque est dédié à Henriette.

HENRIETTE MAJOR • PATRICE DUBUC

Chansons
des quatre saisons

Illustrées par
Philippe Beha, Marie Lafrance,
Luc Melanson, Daniel Sylvestre,
et Marie-Ève Tremblay

Arrangements musicaux
Patrice Dubuc

FIDES

Direction éditoriale ◆ GUYLAINE GIRARD

Direction artistique ◆ GIANNI CACCIA

Direction de production ◆ CAROLE OUIMET

Réalisation des portées musicales ◆ JEAN FITZGERALD

Illustrateurs

Philippe Beha ◆ couverture et pages 20 à 25, 48 à 53, 76-77, 94 à 99, 112 à 116 et 124

Marie Lafrance ◆ pages 10 à 13, 36 à 39, 54 à 57, 78 à 81 et 90 à 93

Luc Melanson ◆ pages 14 à 19, 44 à 47, 66 à 69, 84-85 et 100 à 105

Daniel Sylvestre ◆ pages 32 à 35, 58 à 63, 70 à 75 et 86 à 89

Marie-Ève Tremblay ◆ pages 26 à 31, 40 à 43, 64-65, 82-83 et 106 à 111

Catalogage avant publication de Bibliothèque et Archives nationales du Québec et Bibliothèque et Archives Canada

Vedette principale au titre :
Chansons des quatre saisons
Doit être acc. d'un disque son.
Pour les jeunes.

ISBN 978-2-7621-2775-1

1. Saisons - Chansons et musique - Ouvrages pour la jeunesse. 2. Chansons folkloriques françaises - Ouvrages pour la jeunesse.
3. Chansons enfantines françaises. I. Major, Henriette, 1933-2006. II. Dubuc, Patrice.

M1977.S4C45 2008   J782.42'1524   C2008-941791-7

Dépôt légal : 4ᵉ trimestre 2008
Bibliothèque et Archives nationales du Québec
© Éditions Fides, 2008

Les Éditions Fides reconnaissent l'aide financière du Gouvernement du Canada par l'entremise du Programme d'aide au développement
de l'industrie de l'édition (PADIÉ) pour leurs activités d'édition. Les Éditions Fides remercient de leur soutien financier le Conseil
des Arts du Canada et la Société de développement des entreprises culturelles du Québec (SODEC). Les Éditions Fides bénéficient
du Programme de crédit d'impôt pour l'édition de livres du Gouvernement du Québec, géré par la SODEC.

IMPRIMÉ AU CANADA EN OCTOBRE 2008

Nous saluons le travail passionné d'Henriette Major qui,
au fil des ans, a contribué à garder bien vivantes les plus belles
chansons traditionnelles du répertoire francophone.

Les Éditions Fides

Présentation

Certaines personnes collectionnent les timbres, d'autres les cartes postales ou les papillons. Pour sa part, Henriette Major collectionnait les chansons. Dans sa jeunesse, la tradition orale était bien vivante et son père, Henri, musicien autodidacte qui jouait du violon, de la clarinette et du saxophone, lui a transmis l'amour des chansons et des mélodies.

Henriette l'a communiqué à son tour à ses enfants. D'aussi loin que je me souvienne, nous chantions en famille et je me considère privilégié d'avoir eu cet éveil à la musique et à la poésie quand j'étais tout jeune.

Lorsque j'ai appris que les Éditions Fides étaient intéressées à aller de l'avant avec ce projet qu'Henriette avait élaboré autour du thème des saisons, je n'ai pas hésité bien longtemps. J'ai commencé par me replonger dans l'écoute de certaines versions que nous écoutions en famille dans les années 1960, comme celles des Cailloux (*C'est dans le mois de mai, Au chant de l'alouette*). J'ai aussi écouté Raoul Roy (*Isabeau s'y promène, Les draveurs de la Gatineau*). Raoul était un grand ami d'Henriette ; il m'a également enseigné la guitare à mes débuts.

Pour célébrer les saisons, il y a toujours eu des chansons. Cette sélection comprend des titres variés, qui viennent d'ici et d'ailleurs, car le folklore est sans frontières. Nous sommes fiers de continuer à propager ces trésors de la tradition orale qu'Henriette a contribué à faire connaître.

Patrice Dubuc

Printemps

Les moineaux

Salut, les joyeux moineaux !
Jamais rien ne vous arrête,
ni le vent, ni les tempêtes.
Vous êtes des rigolos !

Vous êtes toujours contents !
Vous n'êtes pas difficiles,
On vous trouve dans les villes
aussi bien que dans les champs.

En été comme en hiver,
Vous bravez les étourneaux
pour ramasser quelques miettes
qu'une brave dame jette.

Votre chant n'est pas très beau ;
on dit que le moineau piaille
et qu'il aime la bataille.
Mais malgré tous vos défauts,
vous êtes les héros
de tous les passereaux.

(Henriette MAJOR, *J'aime les poèmes*, Hurtubise HMH, 2002)

C'est dans le mois de mai

Fine

D.C. al Fine

C'est dans le mois de mai
En montant la rivière
C'est dans le mois de mai
Que les filles sont belles.

Que les filles sont belles, au gué,
Que les filles sont belles.

14

Et que tous les galants
En montant la rivière
Et que tous les galants
Y changent leur princesse.

Y changent leur princesse, au gué,
Y changent leur princesse.

Mais moi, j'ne changerai pas
En montant la rivière
Mais moi, j'ne changerai pas
Car la mienne est trop belle.

Car la mienne est trop belle, au gué,
Car la mienne est trop belle.

Elle a de beaux yeux bleus
En montant la rivière
Elle a de beaux yeux bleus
Une bouche vermeille.

Une bouche vermeille, au gué,
Une bouche vermeille.

Ah ! Qu'il me serait doux
En montant la rivière
Ah! Qu'il me serait doux
De vivre avec elle.

De vivre avec elle, au gué,
De vivre avec elle.

C'est dans le mois de mai
En montant la rivière
C'est dans le mois de mai
Que les filles sont belles.

Gai lon la, gai le rosier

Par der - rièr' chez ma tan - te, Lui y'a t'un bois jo - li.

Le ros - si - gnol y chan - te Et le jour et la nuit.

Gai lon la, gai le ro - sier Du jo - li mois de mai.

Par derrièr' chez ma tante,
Lui y'a t'un bois joli.
Le rossignol y chante
Et le jour et la nuit.

Gai lon la, gai le rosier
Du joli mois de mai.

Il chante pour les belles
Qui n'ont point de mari.
Il ne chante pas pour moi,
Car j'en ai un joli.

Gai lon la, gai le rosier
Du joli mois de mai.

Il n'est pas dans la danse,
Il est bien loin d'ici.
Il est dans la Hollande :
Les Hollandais l'ont pris.

Gai lon la, gai le rosier
Du joli mois de mai.

« Que donneriez-vous, belle,
Qui l'amèn'rait ici ? »
Je donnerais Versailles,
Paris et Saint-Denis !

Gai lon la, gai le rosier
Du joli mois de mai.

Je donnerais Versailles,
Paris et Saint-Denis.
Et la claire fontaine
De mon jardin joli.

Gai lon la, gai le rosier
Du joli mois de mai.

Voici le mois de mai

Voi - ci le mois de mai Où les feuill's vol'nt au vent Voi - ci le mois de mai Où les feuill's vol'nt au vent Où les feuill's vol'nt au vent Si jo - lie mi - gnon - ne Où les feuill's vol'nt au vent Si mi - gnon - ne - ment. Où les feuill's vol'nt au vent Si mi - gnon - ne - ment.

Voici le mois de mai
Où les feuill's vol'nt au vent. } *(bis)*
Où les feuill's vol'nt au vent
Si jolie mignonne
Où les feuill's vol'nt au vent } *(bis)*
Si mignonnement.

Le gentil fils du roi
S'en va les ramassant. } *(bis)*
S'en va les ramassant
Si jolie mignonne
S'en va les ramassant
Si mignonnement. } *(bis)*

Il en ramasse tant
Qu'il en remplit ses gants. } *(bis)*
Qu'il en remplit ses gants
Si jolie mignonne
Qu'il en remplit ses gants
Si mignonnement. } *(bis)*

À sa mie les porta,
Les donna en présent. } *(bis)*
Les donna en présent
Si jolie mignonne
Les donna en présent } *(bis)*
Si mignonnement.

« Prenez, prenez, ma mie, } *(bis)*
Je vous donne ces gants.
Je vous donne ces gants
Si jolie mignonne
Je vous donne ces gants } *(bis)*
Si mignonnement. »

29

« Portez-les donc, ma mie,
Trois ou quatre fois l'an. } *(bis)*
Trois ou quatre fois l'an
Si jolie mignonne
Trois ou quatre fois l'an
Si mignonnement. » } *(bis)*

« À Pâques, à la Toussaint,
À Noël, à Saint-Jean. } *(bis)*
À Noël, à Saint-Jean
Si jolie mignonne
À Noël, à Saint-Jean
Si mignonnement. » } *(bis)*

Ma Normandie

Quand tout re - naît à l'es - pé - ran - ce Et que l'hi - ver fuit loin de nous, Sous

le beau ciel de no - tre Fran - ce Quand le so - leil re - vient plus doux; Quand

la na - ture est re - ver - die, Quand l'hi - ron - delle est de re - tour, J'aime

à re - voir ma Nor - man - di - e, C'est le pa - ys qui m'a don - né le jour.

Quand tout renaît à l'espérance
Et que l'hiver fuit loin de nous,
Sous le beau ciel de notre France
Quand le soleil revient plus doux ;
Quand la nature est reverdie,
Quand l'hirondelle est de retour,
J'aime à revoir ma Normandie,
C'est le pays qui m'a donné le jour.

J'ai vu les champs de l'Helvétie
Et ses chalets et ses glaciers;
J'ai vu le ciel de l'Italie
Et Venise et ses gondoliers.
En saluant chaque patrie
Je me disais: «Aucun séjour
N'est plus beau que ma Normandie,
C'est le pays qui m'a donné le jour.»

Il est un âge dans la vie
Où chaque rêve doit finir,
Un âge où l'âme recueillie
A besoin de se souvenir.
Lorsque ma muse refroidie
Aura fini ses chants d'amour;
J'irai revoir ma Normandie,
C'est le pays qui m'a donné le jour.

À la volette

Mon pe - tit oi - seau — a pris sa vo - lée. Mon pe - tit oi - seau — a pris sa vo - lée. A pris
sa... À la vo - let - te A pris sa... À la vo - let - te A pris sa vo - lée. A pris sa vo - lée.

Mon petit oiseau a pris sa volée. *(bis)*
A pris sa... À la volette *(bis)*
A pris sa volée. *(bis)*

Il prit sa volée sur un oranger. *(bis)*
Sur un o... À la volette *(bis)*
Sur un oranger. *(bis)*

La branche était sèche, l'oiseau est tombé. *(bis)*
L'oiseau est... À la volette *(bis)*
L'oiseau est tombé. *(bis)*

«Mon petit oiseau, où t'es-tu blessé? *(bis)*
Où t'es-tu... À la volette *(bis)*
Où t'es-tu blessé? » *(bis)*

«Me suis cassé l'aile et tordu le pied. *(bis)*
Et tordu... À la volette *(bis)*
Et tordu le pied. » *(bis)*

«Mon petit oiseau, veux-tu te soigner? *(bis)*
Veux-tu te... À la volette *(bis)*
Veux-tu te soigner? » *(bis)*

«Je veux me soigner et me marier. *(bis)*
Et me ma... À la volette *(bis)*
Et me marier. *(bis)*

Me marier bien vite sur un oranger. *(bis)*
Sur un o... À la volette *(bis)*
Sur un oranger. » *(bis)*

Été

Soleil, soleil

Soleil, soleil.
Sur la brillance du ciel,
Les feuilles à l'envers
Dessinent des dentelles.
Un lézard fuit.

Soleil, soleil.
Sur l'exubérance des choses
Et sur nos têtes accablées
À quelques pas d'une eau secrète
D'une fraîcheur insoupçonnée.

(Henriette MAJOR)

Le temps des cerises

Quand nous chan - te - rons le temps des ce - ri - ses Et gai ros - si - gnol, et mer - le mo - queur Se - ront tous en fê - te! Les bel - les au - ront la fo - lie en tê - te Et les a - mou - reux, du so - leil au cœur! Quand nous chan - te - rons le temps des ce - ri - ses Sif - fle - ra bien mieux le mer - le mo - queur!

Quand nous chanterons le temps des cerises
Et gai rossignol, et merle moqueur
Seront tous en fête !
Les belles auront la folie en tête
Et les amoureux, du soleil au cœur !
Quand nous chanterons le temps des cerises
Sifflera bien mieux le merle moqueur !

Mais il est bien court le temps des cerises
Où l'on s'en va deux, cueillir en rêvant
Des pendants d'oreilles...
Cerises d'amour, aux robes pareilles,
Tombant sous la feuille en gouttes de sang...
Mais il est bien court le temps des cerises,
Pendants de corail qu'on cueille en rêvant !

Quand vous en serez au temps des cerises
Si vous avez peur des chagrins d'amour,
Évitez les belles !
Moi qui ne crains pas les peines cruelles,
Je ne vivrai point sans souffrir un jour...
Quand vous en serez au temps des cerises
Vous aurez aussi des peines d'amour !

J'aimerai toujours le temps des cerises :
C'est de ce temps-là que je garde au cœur
Une plaie ouverte !
Et Dame Fortune en m'étant offerte
Ne pourra jamais fermer ma douleur...
J'aimerai toujours le temps des cerises
Et le souvenir que je garde au cœur !

Gentil coquelicot

J'ai des - cen - du dans mon jar - din   J'ai des - cen -
du dans mon jar - din   Pour y cueil - lir du ro - ma - rin.
Gen - til co - qu'li - cot, Mes - da - mes, Gen - til co - qu'li - cot nou - veau!

J'ai descendu dans mon jardin *(bis)*
Pour y cueillir du romarin.
Gentil coqu'licot, Mesdames,
Gentil coqu'licot nouveau !

Pour y cueillir du romarin *(bis)*
J'n'en avais pas cueilli trois brins.
Gentil coqu'licot, Mesdames,
Gentil coqu'licot nouveau !

J'n'en avais pas cueilli trois brins *(bis)*
Qu'un rossignol vint sur ma main.
Gentil coqu'licot, Mesdames,
Gentil coqu'licot nouveau !

Qu'un rossignol vint sur ma main *(bis)*
Il me dit trois mots en latin.
Gentil coqu'licot, Mesdames,
Gentil coqu'licot nouveau !

Il me dit trois mots en latin *(bis)*
Que les hommes ne valent rien.
Gentil coqu'licot, Mesdames,
Gentil coqu'licot nouveau!

Que les hommes ne valent rien *(bis)*
Et les garçons encore bien moins.
Gentil coqu'licot, Mesdames,
Gentil coqu'licot nouveau!

Et les garçons encore bien moins *(bis)*
Des dames, il ne me dit rien.
Gentil coqu'licot, Mesdames,
Gentil coqu'licot nouveau!

Des dames, il ne me dit rien *(bis)*
Mais des d'moiselles beaucoup de bien.
Gentil coqu'licot, Mesdames,
Gentil coqu'licot nouveau!

Et moi de m'encourir

En pas - sant près d'un p'tit bois Où le cou - cou chan - tait Dans son jo -
li chant, il di - sait: «Cou - cou, cou - cou Cou - cou, cou - cou» Et moi qui cro - yais qu'il di - sait: «Coup' lui le
cou! Coup' lui le cou!» Et moi de m'en - cour', cour', Et moi de m'en - cou - rir.

En passant près d'un p'tit bois
Où le coucou chantait;
Dans son joli chant, il disait:
— Coucou, coucou *(bis)*
Et moi qui croyais qu'il disait:
— Coup'lui le cou! *(bis)*

Refrain
Et moi de m'encour', cour',
Et moi de m'encourir.

En passant près d'un étang
Où le canard chantait ;
Dans son joli chant, il disait :
— Cancan, cancan *(bis)*
Et moi qui croyais qu'il disait :
— Jett'le dedans ! *(bis)*

Refrain

En passant près d'un moulin
Où un' femme berçait ;
Dans son joli chant, elle disait :
— Dodo, dodo *(bis)*
Et moi qui croyais qu'elle disait :
— Jett'le dans l'eau ! *(bis)*

Refrain

En passant près d'une rivière
Où les pêcheurs pêchaient ;
Dans leur joli chant, ils disaient :
— Quel beau poisson ! *(bis)*
Et moi qui croyais qu'ils disaient :
— Quel polisson ! *(bis)*

Refrain

Isabeau s'y promène

I - sa - beau s'y pro - mè - ne le long de son jar - din.

Le long de son jar - din, sur le bord de l'i - le,

Le long de son jar - din, sur le bord de l'eau, Sur le bord du ruis - seau.

Isabeau s'y promène le long de son jardin.
Le long de son jardin, sur le bord de l'île,
Le long de son jardin, sur le bord de l'eau,
Sur le bord du ruisseau.

Elle fit une rencontre de trente matelots.
De trente matelots, sur le bord de l'île,
De trente matelots, sur le bord de l'eau,
Sur le bord du ruisseau.

Le plus jeune des trente, il se mit à chanter.
Il se mit à chanter, sur le bord de l'île,
Il se mit à chanter, sur le bord de l'eau,
Sur le bord du ruisseau.

« La chanson que tu chantes, je voudrais la savoir.
Je voudrais la savoir, sur le bord de l'île,
Je voudrais la savoir, sur le bord de l'eau,
Sur le bord du ruisseau. »

« Embarquez dans ma barque, je vous la chanterai.
Je vous la chanterai, sur le bord de l'île,
Je vous la chanterai, sur le bord de l'eau,
Sur le bord du ruisseau. »

Quand elle fut dans la barque, elle se mit à pleurer.
Elle se mit à pleurer, sur le bord de l'île,
Elle se mit à pleurer, sur le bord de l'eau,
Sur le bord du ruisseau.

« Qu'avez-vous donc la belle, qu'avez-vous à pleurer ?
Qu'avez-vous à pleurer, sur le bord de l'île,
Qu'avez-vous à pleurer, sur le bord de l'eau,
Sur le bord du ruisseau. »

« Je pleure mon anneau d'or, dans l'eau, il est tombé.
Dans l'eau, il est tombé, sur le bord de l'île,
Dans l'eau, il est tombé, sur le bord de l'eau,
Sur le bord du ruisseau. »

« Ne pleurez point, la belle, je vous le plongerai.
Je vous le plongerai, sur le bord de l'île,
Je vous le plongerai, sur le bord de l'eau,
Sur le bord du ruisseau. »

À la première plonge, il n'a rien ramené.
Il n'a rien ramené, sur le bord de l'île,
Il n'a rien ramené, sur le bord de l'eau,
Sur le bord du ruisseau.

À la seconde plonge, l'anneau a voltigé.
L'anneau a voltigé, sur le bord de l'île,
L'anneau a voltigé, sur le bord de l'eau,
Sur le bord du ruisseau.

À la troisième plonge, le galant s'est noyé.
Le galant s'est noyé, sur le bord de l'île,
Le galant s'est noyé, sur le bord de l'eau,
Sur le bord du ruisseau.

Au chant de l'alouette

On m'en-voie au champ, c'est pour y cueil - lir On m'en-voie au champ, c'est pour y cueil - lir Je n'ai point cueil - li, j'ai cher - ché des nids. Au chant de l'a - lou - et - te, Je veil - le, je dors, J'é - cou - te l'a - lou - ette Et puis je m'en - dors.

On m'envoie au champ, c'est pour y cueillir. *(bis)*
Je n'ai point cueilli, j'ai cherché des nids.

Refrain
Au chant de l'alouette,
Je veille, je dors,
J'écoute l'alouette
Et puis je m'endors.

Je n'ai point cueilli, j'ai cherché des nids. *(bis)*
J'ai trouvé la caille assise sur son nid.

Refrain

J'ai trouvé la caille assise sur son nid. *(bis)*
J'lui marchai sur l'aile et la lui rompis.

Refrain

J'lui marchai sur l'aile et la lui rompis. *(bis)*
Elle m'a dit : « Pucelle, retire-toi d'ici. »

Refrain

Elle m'a dit : « Pucelle, retire-toi d'ici. » *(bis)*
« Je n'suis pas pucelle », que j'lui répondis.

Refrain

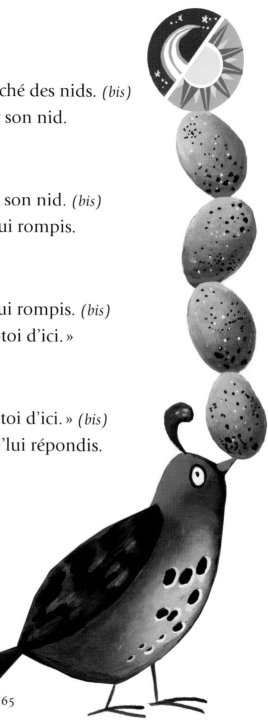

Automne

Bel automne (13)

Parcourant les chemins fabuleux de l'automne,
J'y ai trouvé de l'or, du cuivre et de l'étain,
Des lambeaux de velours et d'antiques satins.

Parcourant les chemins enchantés de l'automne,
Je me suis enroulée dans la brume d'argent
Et mes pieds s'enfonçaient dans un tapis persan.

Parcourant les chemins parfumés de l'automne,
De rustiques odeurs s'exhalaient sous mes pas
Et s'évanouissaient avant que je les nomme.

Parcourant les chemins somptueux de l'automne,
J'ai voulu ramasser ces trésors à pleins bras.
Mais, ces trésors-là meurent qu'on les emprisonne.

Parcourant les chemins dénudés de l'automne,
J'ai vu fuir les oiseaux et pleurer les lilas
Et j'ai dû m'inventer du feu contre le froid.

(Henriette MAJOR)

Les draveurs de la Gatineau

A - dieu char - man - tes rives Du beau Ka - ké - bon - guay.

Voi - là le temps qu'ar - rive Il faut nous sé - pa - rer. L'hi - ver va

s'ins - tal - ler Et tous ses em - bar - ras. Cent hommes sont

ras - sem - blés Jack Boyd les con - dui - ra. Jack Boyd les con - dui - ra.

Adieu charmantes rives
Du beau Kakébonguay.
Voilà le temps qu'arrive
Il faut nous séparer.
L'hiver va s'installer
Et tous ses embarras.
Cent hommes sont rassemblés
Jack Boyd les conduira. *(bis)*

Hivernant, tu nous quittes
Ton sac dessus le dos.
Tu nous quittes trop vite,
Tu maudis nos billots.
Tu maudis nos rivières,
Nos rames, nos avirons.
Tu maudis jusqu'à l'air
Que nous respirerons. *(bis)*

Sautons chutes et rapides,
Nageons adroitement.
Courons sur la lisière
Qui suit le grand courant.
Arrivés au désert,
Bourgoin nous attend là.
Dessus le gazon vert,
C'est lui qui traitera. *(bis)*

Buvons chers camarades
À la santé de Boyd ;
Trois ou quatre rasades
Et donnons-lui la main.
Dravons la Gatineau,
Dravons-la jusqu'en bas
Où nos barges sur l'eau
Vont mieux qu'un rabaska. *(bis)*

Le grand cerf

Dans sa maison, un grand cerf
Regardait par la fenêtre
Un lapin venir au loin
Et frapper chez lui.
— Cerf, cerf, ouvre-moi
Ou le chasseur me tuera !
— Lapin, lapin entre et viens
Me serrer la main.

Allons, chasseur, vite en campagne

Mes a - mis, par - tons pour la chas - se. Du cor, j'en - tends le joy - eux son. Ton

ton, ton ton, ton tai - ne, ton ton Ja - mais ce plai - sir ne nous las - se,

Il est bien en tou - tes sai - sons. Ton ton, ton tai - ne, ton ton.

Mes amis, partons pour la chasse.
Du cor, j'entends le joyeux son.
Ton ton, ton ton, ton taine, ton ton,
Jamais ce plaisir ne nous lasse,
Il est bien en toutes saisons.
Ton ton, ton taine, ton ton.

Le vrai chasseur est plein d'audace.
Il est gai, joyeux et luron.
Ton ton, ton ton, ton taine, ton ton,
Mais quelque fanfare qu'il fasse,
Le chasseur n'est pas fanfaron.
Ton ton, ton taine, ton ton.

Pour suivre le chevreuil qui passe,
Il parcourt le bois, le vallon.
Ton ton, ton ton, ton taine, ton ton,
Et jamais en suivant sa trace
Il ne trouve le chemin long.
Ton ton, ton taine, ton ton.

Quand on a terminé la chasse,
Le chasseur se rend au grand Rond.
Ton ton, ton ton, ton taine, ton ton,
Et chacun boit à pleine tasse
Au grand saint Hubert, son patron.
Ton ton, ton taine, ton ton.

Vent frais, vent du matin

Vent frais Vent du ma - tin Vent qui souffle Au

som - met des grands pins. Joie du vent qui passe Al - lons dans le grand...

Vent frais
Vent du matin.
Vent qui souffle
Au sommet des grands pins.
Joie du vent qui passe
Allons dans le grand...

Vent frais
Vent du matin,
etc...

La trompe sonne dans les bois

La trom- pe son- ne dans les bois L'ar- den- te meu- te pas- se. Chasseurs bril-lants, pi-queurs a-droits S'é-lan- cent à la fois. En-ten- dez-vous de
tren- te voix Le bruit qui frappe l'es-pa- ce Taï- aut! Le cerf est
aux a-bois, Il meurt, il meurt, je crois. Ah! que la chas- se
Soit le plai-sir des Rois! Ah! que la chas-se Soit le plai-sir des Rois!

La trompe sonne dans les bois,
L'ardente meute passe.
Chasseurs brillants, piqueurs adroits
S'élancent à la fois.

Entendez-vous de trente voix
Le bruit qui frappe l'espace.
Taïaut ! Le cerf est aux abois,
Il meurt, il meurt, je crois.

Ah ! que la chasse
Soit le plaisir des Rois !
Ah ! que la chasse
Soit le plaisir des Rois !

Hiver

Le vent d'hiver (19)

Je suis le vent d'hiver.
Je fais danser la neige.
Je mène le cortège
Des plaisirs de l'hiver.

Je dégage la place
Pour les joyeux skieurs.
Je prépare la glace
Pour tous les patineurs.

Les ours dans leur tanière
S'endorment loin du froid.
Les écureuils préfèrent
S'amuser avec moi.

Dans la cour d'école,
Mes amis, les enfants,
Avec la neige molle,
Font un bonhomme blanc.

(Henriette MAJOR)

La guignolée

Bon - jour le maître et la mai - tres - se Et tout le mond' de la mai - son.

Pour le der - nier jour de l'an - née__ La gui - gno - lée vous nous de - vez.

Si vous vou - lez rien nous don - ner, Di - tes - nous lé.__

On em - mè - ne - ra seu - le - ment La fille aï - née.__

Refrain

Bonjour le maître et la maîtresse } *(bis)*
Et tout le mond' de la maison.

Pour le dernier jour de l'année } *(bis)*
La guignolée vous nous devez.

Si vous voulez rien nous donner, } *(bis)*
Dites-nous lé.
On emmènera seulement } *(bis)*
La fille aînée.

Refrain

On lui fera faire bonne chère, } *(bis)*
On lui fera chauffer les pieds. }

On vous demande seulement } *(bis)*
Une chignée }
De vingt à trente pieds de long, } *(bis)*
Si vous voulez. }

Refrain

La guignolée, la guignoloche } *(bis)*
Mettez du lard dedans ma poche. }

Quand nous fûmes au milieu du bois, } *(bis)*
Nous fûmes à l'ombre. }
J'entendis chanter le coucou } *(bis)*
Et la colombe. }

Refrain

Rossignolet du vert bocage, } *(bis)*
Rossignolet du bois joli. }

Eh ! Va-t-en dire à ma maîtresse } *(bis)*
Que j'meurs pour ses beaux yeux. }

HIVER

La marche des Rois Mages

De bon ma - tin, j'ai ren - con - tré le train De trois grands Rois qui al - laient en vo - ya - ge, De

bon ma - tin, j'ai ren - con - tré le train De trois grands Rois des - sus le grand che - min. Ve -

naient d'a - bord Des gar - des du corps, Des gens ar - més a - vec tren - te pe - tits pa - ges, Ve -

naient d'a - bord Des gar - des du corps, Des gens ar - més des - sus leurs jus - tau - corps.

De bon matin, j'ai rencontré le train
De trois grands Rois qui allaient en voyage.
De bon matin, j'ai rencontré le train
De trois grands Rois dessus le grand chemin.
Venaient d'abord
Des gardes du corps,
Des gens armés avec trente petits pages.
Venaient d'abord
Des gardes du corps,
Des gens armés dessus leurs justaucorps.

95

Puis sur un char doré de toutes parts,

On voit trois Rois modestes comme des anges.

Puis sur un char doré de toutes parts,

Trois Rois debout parmi les étendards.

L'étoile luit

Et les Rois conduit

Par longs chemins devant une pauvre étable.

L'étoile luit

Et les Rois conduit

Par longs chemins devant l'humble réduit.

Au Fils de Dieu qui naquit en ce lieu,
Ils viennent tous présenter leurs hommages.
Au Fils de Dieu qui naquit en ce lieu,
Ils viennent tous présenter leurs doux vœux.
De beaux présents,
Or, myrrhe et encens,
Ils vont offrir au maître tant aimable.
De beaux présents,
Or, myrrhe et encens,
Ils vont offrir au bienheureux enfant.

La légende de saint Nicolas

Ils é - taient trois pe - tits en - fants Qui s'en al - laient gla - ner aux champs.

Tant sont al - lés tant sont ve - nus, Que sur le soir se sont per -

dus. S'en sont al - lés chez le bou - cher: «Bou - cher vou - drais - tu nous lo - ger?»

Refrain

Ils étaient trois petits enfants
Qui s'en allaient glaner aux champs.

Tant sont allés tant sont venus,
Que sur le soir se sont perdus.
S'en sont allés chez le boucher :
« Boucher voudrais-tu nous loger ? »

Refrain

101

« Entrez, entrez petits enfants
Il y a d'la place assurément. »
Ils n'étaient pas sitôt entrés,
Que le boucher les a tués.
Refrain

Saint Nicolas au bout d'sept ans
Vint à passer dedans ce champ,
Alla frapper chez le boucher :
« Boucher voudrais-tu me loger ? »
Refrain

« Entrez, entrez, saint Nicolas,
Il y a d'la place, il n'en manqu' pas. »
Il n'était pas sitôt entré
Qu'il a demandé à souper.
Refrain

On lui apporte du jambon.
Il n'en veut pas, il n'est pas bon.
On lui apporte du rôti.
Il n'en veut pas, il n'est pas cuit.
Refrain

« Du p'tit salé, je veux avoir,
Qu'il y a sept ans qu'est au saloir. »
Quand le boucher entendit ça,
Bien vivement il se sauva.
Refrain

« Petits enfants qui dormez là,
Je suis le grand saint Nicolas. »
Le grand saint étendit trois doigts,
Les trois enfants ressuscita.
Refrain

Le premier dit : « J'ai bien dormi. »
Le second dit : « Et moi aussi. »
A ajouté le plus petit :
« Je croyais être au paradis. »
Refrain

Joseph est bien marié

Jo - seph est bien ma - ri - é   À la fil - le de Jes - sé

Jo - seph est bien ma - ri - é   À la fil - le de Jes - sé

C'é - tait cho - se bien nou - vel - le, Que d'ê - tre mère et pu - cel - le.

Dieu y a bien o - pé - ré: Jo - seph est bien ma - ri - é.

Joseph est bien marié   }
À la fille de Jessé.   *(bis)*

C'était chose bien nouvelle,
Que d'être mère et pucelle.
Dieu y a bien opéré :
Joseph est bien marié.

Et quand ce vint au premier
Que Dieu nous voulut sauver. } *(bis)*
Il fit en terre descendre
Son cher fils Jésus pour prendre
En Marie humanité :
Joseph est bien marié.

Quand Joseph eut aperçu
Que Marie avait conçu, } *(bis)*
Il lui dit : « Ma bonne amie
Certes digne ne suis mie,
D'être à vous apparié. »
Joseph est bien marié.

À Noël sur les minuit,
La Vierge enfanta son fruit. } *(bis)*
Sans lit, traversin ni couche
De ce lieu, elle ne bouge,
Où son âme était liée :
Joseph est bien marié.

Quand il neige sur mon pays

Quand il nei - ge sur mon pa - ys, De gros flo - cons cou - vrent les
bran - ches, Et les re - gards sont é - blou - is Par la clar - té des rou - tes
blan - ches. Et dans les champs en - se - ve - lis, La ter - re re - prend son grand
som - me Qu'elle fait pour mieux nour - rir l'hom - me, Quand il nei - ge sur mon pa - ys.

Quand il neige sur mon pays,
De gros flocons couvrent les branches,
Et les regards sont éblouis
Par la clarté des routes blanches.
Et dans les champs ensevelis,
La terre reprend son grand somme
Qu'elle fait pour mieux nourrir l'homme,
Quand il neige sur mon pays.

Quand il neige sur mon pays,
On voit s'ébattre dans les rues
Les petits enfants réjouis
Par tant de splendeurs reparues.
Et ce sont des appels, des cris,
Des extases et des délirs,
Des courses, des jeux et des rires,
Quand il neige sur mon pays.

Quand il neige sur mon pays,
C'est tout le ciel qui se disperse
Sur la montagne et les toits gris
Qu'il revêt de sa claire averse.
Sous l'avalanche de ses lis,
D'un pur éclat, il nous inonde.
C'est le plus beau pays du monde,
Quand il neige sur mon pays.

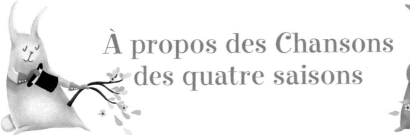

À propos des Chansons des quatre saisons

PRINTEMPS

Page 14 · C'est dans le mois de mai

Cette chanson est un classique du folklore canadien-français.
Elle est aussi connue sous le titre « En montant la rivière ».

Page 20 · Gai lon la, gai le rosier

Cette chanson est aussi connue sous le titre
« Le Rossignol y chante ». Il existe plusieurs
chansons utilisant le thème du rossignol
porteur d'un message d'amour.

Page 27 · Voici le mois de mai

Une des nombreuses chansons créées pour fêter
le mois de mai et le retour du beau temps. Autrefois,
dans les campagnes, il était d'usage de souligner
l'arrivée du mois de mai en plantant, devant
la porte de celle que l'on voulait épouser,
un mai enrubanné.

Page 33 • Ma Normandie

Cette chanson date de la fin du XIXe siècle. Elle raconte
la nostalgie de tous ceux qui s'exilent loin de leur région
natale. Au Québec, elle évoque justement les origines
normandes de nombreuses familles.

Page 36 • À la volette

Voici une chanson très ancienne,
qui se chante sur un rythme enjoué.

ÉTÉ

Page 45 • Le temps des cerises

Cette chanson d'amour a été composée par
J.-B. Clément, à Montmartre, en 1866.

Page 48 • Gentil coquelicot

Cette chanson à l'air guilleret et aux
paroles malicieuses nous vient de Touraine,
qu'on nomme aussi le jardin de la France.
Elle date du règne de Louis XV.

AUTOMNE

Page 71 • Les draveurs de la Gatineau

Autrefois au Québec, le transport du bois se faisait
par flottage : des hommes, munis de grands bâtons
et sautant de billots en billots et de roches
en roches, dirigeaient le bois sur les grands cours
d'eau jusqu'à destination de l'usine où il était traité.
Cette action de conduire le bois se nomme « la drave ».

Page 76 • Le grand cerf

Cette comptine chantée est souvent accompagnée d'une gestuelle qui mime,
suivant les mots de la chanson, l'action des différents personnages.

Page 79 • Allons, chasseur, vite en campagne

Cette vieille chanson française est à la fois une
chanson de chasse et une chanson de marche.
Les intervalles mélodiques rappellent l'appel
du clairon.

Page 82 • **Vent frais, vent du matin**

Ce canon à trois voix a été composé
dans les années 1940-1950.

Page 84 • **La trompe sonne dans les bois**

La trompe ou cor de chasse sert à transmettre,
à de grandes distances, toutes les péripéties
de la chasse au moyen de sons ayant
chacun une signification déterminée.
On ne l'emploie que dans la Grande chasse
ou Chasse à Courre où elle sert aussi
à guider les chiens.

HIVER

Page 90 • La guignolée

Le mot «guignolée» désigne à la fois une
coutume et une chanson. Autrefois, dans
les campagnes québécoises, on chantait
cette chanson en passant par les maisons
pour cueillir des dons pour les pauvres.
Cette coutume avait lieu au début de l'année,
autour du Jour de l'an.

Page 94 • La marche des Rois Mages

Les paroles de cette ancienne chanson sont d'Alphonse Daudet
et la musique, de Georges Bizet sur un air de Lully, célèbre compositeur
du siècle de Louis XIV qui fut le premier à introduire des airs de marche
dans les opéras et les ballets.

Page 101 • La légende de saint Nicolas

Saint Nicolas était évêque à Myre, en Turquie, au IVe siècle.
Il est le patron des marins d'eau douce, des tonneliers,
des parfumeurs, des apothicaires et, à cause de la légende
d'où est tirée cette chanson, des enfants. Dans la
mythologie enfantine des pays nordiques,
il est le Père Noël.

Page 107 • Joseph est bien marié

Cette chanson vient de la région de Champagne
et a été composée au XVIe siècle. Les paroles
sont de Ducaurot, maître de chapelle
de Henri IV.

Page 112 • Quand il neige sur mon pays

Les paroles de cette chanson ont été composées
par un des grands poètes du Québec,
Albert Lozeau (1878-1924). Cette chanson
fait souvent partie du répertoire des chorales
au Québec.

Index

Table des matières

Automne

Hiver

Cet ouvrage a été achevé d'imprimer en octobre 2008
sur les presses de l'imprimerie Transcontinental (Canada)

RANGES OF ROMANTICISM

RANGES OF ROMANTICISM

Five for Ten Studies

With Introductions, Notes,
& Commentaries by

Thomas Meade Harwell

Longwood Academic
Wakefield, New Hampshire

Published in 1991 by Longwood Academic, a division of Hollowbrook Communications, Inc., Wakefield, New Hampshire, 03872-0757, U.S.A.

Library of Congress Cataloging in Publication Data:

Harwell, Thomas Meade.
   Ranges of romanticism : five for ten studies : with introductions, notes & commentaries / by Thomas Meade Harwell.
      p.   cm.
   Includes bibliographical references.
   ISBN 0-89341-604-5 (cloth)
   1. Romanticism. 2. Gothic revival (Literature) 3. Literature.
Modern--History and criticism. I. Title.
PN56.R7H37   1991
809'.9145--dc 20   *90-20190*
                                                              CIP

ACKNOWLEDGMENTS

I. Presentations and Publications

These studies have been presented, with minor differences in wording, at the College English Association, the Popular Culture and American Culture associations, and the Southwest Popular Culture Association; also, at the Arkansas, the Mississippi, and the Tennessee philological associations. Three of the studies have been published: "Wordsworth and Keats: Empiricists" and "Toward a Gothic Metaphysics: Parts" in the *Publications of the Arkansas Philological Association (PAPA),* and "Maurice Levy's *'Structures Profondes'* in the Gothic Novel" in *The English Gothic Novel: A Miscellany* (Salzburg: Universitat Salzburg, 1987). My gratitude is entire to *PAPA* and to the Universitat Salzburg for allowing these studies to appear in *Ranges of Romanticism.*

II. People

To my profit, Carl Woodring and Emery Neff, Columbia emeriti, and Eliseo Vivas, Northwestern emeritus, have given these studies their analytical eye; Robert Lowrey, University of Central Arkansas, Dan Ford, Southern Arkansas University, and George Peek, Arkansas State University, have helpfully supplied much and taken away more in several studies; and William O.S. Sutherland, University of Texas-Austin, ever patient with flaw, has granted survival to the Gothic studies. To these men of knowledge and benevolence, I express thanks and gratitude.

I express gratitude also to library personnel helping along my research. I particularly cite those of the library of Columbia University, of the University of Texas-Pan American, of the Arkansas State University, and, during recent years as visiting scholar on campus, of the University of Texas-Austin. Among that personnel, always a guide out of the maze, I would single out the special benefit of the members of Reference in UT-Austin's Perry-Castaneda Library and those of the Harry Ransom Humanities Research Center.

Last words, but not least, must include thank-you's to Joanne Hawkins and Jerry Bishop of Perry-Castaneda, Winona Thiel of Arkansas State University, and Barbara Tullos of Austin. They have attended with competence and tact my outcry for carrel, locker, manuscript, and computer-menu. Without them, I could not have arrived at the end of *Ranges of Romanticism*.

III. Copyrights

For granting permission to publish copyright material the author expresses appreciation to:

The Arkansas Philological Association and to Robert Lowrey, editor of the *Publications of the Arkansas Philological Association* for "Wordsworth and Keats: Empiricists" [First published, *PAPA,* IV, No. 2 (1978), 26-36]; and for "Toward a Gothic Metaphysics: Parts" [First published, *PAPA,* XII (Fall, 1986), 33-43].

The *Corpus Christi Caller-Times* for the obituary of Severiano G. Barrera, Sr. (First published, the *Corpus Christi Caller-Times,* December 17, 1959, page 16 of Section C).

The Oxford University Press for citations of Keats's letters. Reprinted by permission of the publishers from *The Letters of John Keats,* edited by Maurice Buxton Forman. Copyright 1931 by the Oxford University Press.

The Universitat Salzburg and to Dr. James Hogg, editor of the Salzburg Studies in English Literature, for Statements 5 and 9, Volume II, pages 4, 5 and 8, in "Seventeen on the English Gothic Novel"; and for Statement 7, Volume III, page 3, in "Thirteen on the English Gothic Novel." Reprinted by permission of the publisher and the editor from *The English Gothic Novel: A Miscellany* in four volumes. Copyright 1986, 1987 by the Universitat Salzburg.

The Universitat Salzburg and to Dr. James Hogg, editor of the Salzburg

Studies in English Literature for "Maurice Levy's *Structures Profondes* in the Gothic Novel" by Thomas Meade Harwell. Reprinted by permission of the publisher and the editor from *The English Gothic Novel: A Miscellany,* Volume IV, pages 268-277. Copyright 1986, 1987 by the Universitat Salzburg.

The Universitat Salzburg and to Dr. James Hogg, editor of the Salzburg Studies in English Literature, for facts and notes by Thomas Meade Harwell in "The Pre-Raphaelite," "The Grecian Poet," and "The Pure Artist." Reprinted by permission of the publisher and the author from *Keats and the Critics 1848-1900,* pages 163-234. Copyright 1972 by Thomas Meade Harwell. Reprinted by arrangement with the author and the Salzburg Studies in English Literature, Universitat Salzburg.

The author acknowledges with appreciation the use of citations and collations from the following studies:

To Archon Books for passages in *Military Memoirs,* pages 88 and 183, by (Denis) Charles Parquin, edited and translated by B.T. Jones. (First published, *Souvenirs et campagnes d'un vieux soldat de l'empire.* Paris: Berger-Levrault et Cie, 1892; translated in English by B.T. Jones as *Military Memoirs* by Charles Parquin. London, Longman, n.d.; reprinted, Hamden, CT: Archon Books, 1969.)

To The Belknap Press of Harvard University Press and to Jack Stillinger, editor of *The Poems of John Keats,* for collations of dates, long and short titles, capitalized and lower-case lettering, and punctuation with those in *The Poems of John Keats,* edited by Ernest De Selincourt [London: Methuen, 1905]. (First published, Cambridge: Harvard Univ. Press, 1978.)

To The Clarendon Press of the Oxford University and to H. W. Garrod, editor of *The Poetical Works of John Keats,* for collations of dates, long and short titles, capitalized and lower-case lettering, and punctuation with those in *The Poems of John Keats,* edited by Ernest De Selincourt [London: Methuen, 1905]. (First published, Oxford: Clarendon Press, 1939).

To Cornell University Press for the citation, page 11, from *John Keats's Fancy* by James Ralston Caldwell. (First published, Ithaca: Cornell Univ. Press, 1945.)

To Harvard University Press for citations of Keats's letters from *The Letters of John Keats,* edited by Hyder Edward Rollins. (First published, Cambridge: Harvard Univ. Press, 1958.)

To Longman and Company and to Miriam Allott, editor of *The Poems of John Keats,* for collations of dates, long and short titles, capitalized and lower-case lettering, and punctuation with those in *The Poems of John Keats,* edited by Ernest De Selincourt [London: Methuen, 1905]. (First published, London: Longman, 1970.)

To Methuen and Company and to Routledge, Chapman, and Hall, Inc.

for citations of Keats's poem from *The Poems of John Keats,* edited by Ernest De Selincourt. (First published, London: Methuen, 1905.)

To Methuen and Company and to Routledge, Chapman, and Hall, Inc. for citations in "Notes," pages 389 and 407, by Ernest De Selincourt. (First published, in *The Poems of John Keats,* edited by Ernest De Selincourt. London: Methuen, 1905.)

To A. Nelson Company for the citation, page 64, from *Napoleon in His Times,* edited in French by Jean Savant; translated into English and edited by Katherine Jean. (First published in English, New York: A. Nelson, 1958.)

Table of Contents

PREFACE

If I were asked to name the four ideas of monumental significance in literature—if I were asked not to include bottom-line basics like truth and beauty, pleasure and pain, nature and art, and God and man—I would have to say, next rung up, Classicism, Realism, Symbolism, and Romanticism. Of these, Classicism is the most controlled; Romanticism, the most dispersed. Symbolism is the most "literary" in doing what literature does best; Realism is the least "literary" in being closest to the day-to-day riot.

Of the four, Realism is the most precise and literal, Symbolism the least; Classicism has the most obvious limits, and Romanticism the least. Still, both have limits, as do Realism and Symbolism, and enduring kudos will go to the scholar or critic who makes that fact evident to us all.

I would pass by Realism and Symbolism for the moment to concentrate upon Classicism and Romanticism. Of the four ideas, they have greatest range in possessing ultimate significance as a civilization, yet ultimate minuteness as, say, a diminished couplet. The ideas have a way of embodying all knowledge introduced by man; they also have a way of tolerating all expressions known to man. I illustrate. It is possible for Classicism to refer not only to a civilization, but also to a style, a content, a sublimity sought, and a grossness refuted. It can refer to a painter, musician, or mathematician, or a symphony, play, or logarithm. Classicism can define temperament or influence attitude. Classicism, bound to its credo of clarity, precision, and simplicity, is the master of rules and the progenitor of reason. I go no farther except to say that Romanticism, without picking up the pieces rejected by Classicism, can, in another way, refer as dimensionally and resourcefully to phenomena as Classicism. In one sense, Romanticism is the younger brother of Classicism, with the vocation to express what Classicism cannot. In another sense,

Romanticism is of its own kind, existing no matter what the state of Classicism is. How fortunate, then, that we have allowed them to co-exist, for each helps to define the other, and each needs the other for the liberating or disciplining force it does not itself possess.

I am a specialist in Romanticism, a fact that compels me to know something about Classicism, and, indeed, about Romanticism's niece Symbolism and Classicism's nephew Realism. But, as a specialist, I am compelled to know something about Classicism for my survival as a Romanticist. In brief, I need Classicism to fight the bats of overflow, vagueness, and wordiness that can destroy my Romanticist world. I need Classicism to control values I cannot handle and to define genres that, from lack of volition or knowledge, I would succumb to. On the other hand, I need Classicism only to be rid of it when I am ready to create, or to seek further worlds to plunder, explore, or imagine. I need Classicism to advise my niece on her peril, vagueness. I do not need Classicism when I am ready to condemn the trivia and repetitions of a hackneyed Realism.

Shall I go on? As a Romanticist, I can ignore Symbolism's symbols; as a Classicist, I can ignore Realism's realities. On the other hand, neither Symbolism nor Realism can ignore their ever-watchful uncles. Symbolism and Realism are, indeed, the pawns of their kin and have no alternative to be something else.

I have taken this discussion as far as I would take it, but will add, to finish up, that I have not needed to include literary tropes like archetype, metaphor, or sign; or genre intrinsics like character, action, and plot; or literary events like the latest movement in France or the oldest movement in Japan. Symbolism and Realism will take care of them; or, if not, Classicism and Romanticism. One may say the same for most of the literary terminology in the *Princeton Encyclopedia of Poetry and Poetics.* My point is, we should give thanks for the mega-ranges Classicism and Romanticism; thereafter, for the mini-ranges Realism and Symbolism. Most of the literary ideas outside these four is to the side until planets change, man is reconstructed, and Earth's centers have become Saturn's.

Big statements, seriously said.

So, what am I about in *Ranges of Romanticism?* Obviously, I am about *ranges.* I cite you five: Nature, Poet, Hero, Gothic, and Folklore. Three of the five—Nature, Poet, and Hero—are major in Romanticism, and one, Nature, has received major treatment here.

Gothic and folklore are not major in the Romantic canon, but have been given major attention in *Ranges of Romanticism.* Thus, in "Toward a Gothic Metaphysics: Parts and Postscripts" I would construct a Gothic aesthetic. In "New Light on Pedro Jaramillo," I would locate the *curandero,* a familiar of folklore, in his nature setting. The process has Pedro Jaramillo developed from noble savage to religious *medico.*

Keats, more than Wordsworth, is the central poet in *Ranges of Romanticism.* His nature concepts are identified and connected in "Keats and Nature"; his leaning on empiricism in "Wordsworth and Keats: Empiricists" is jostled against his leaning on beauty in "Keats's Victorian Apostleship." Napoleon's characterization is not that of the Romantic Hero, but of a variant, the Noble Outlaw. I call your attention to the ease with which characteristics of a literary type hold up to describe a political and social hero of the Age.

Perhaps I should regret the brevity of *Ranges of Romanticism* as a book, and the brevity of some studies under Nature and Gothic. Perhaps I should regret also the length of "Keats and Nature" and "New Light on Pedro Jaramillo." Matter of fact, I do not. Just as *Ranges of Romanticism* constitutes the beginning of a project that, to become complete, would require many other ranges of Romanticism, so do "Keats and Nature" and "New Light on Pedro Jaramillo" constitute the completion of two ranges beside which the shorter studies may seem like commentary. I say, crack your jaws against "Conversations on Nature" and "Gothic Postscripts" to determine their survival as topics begun; then test your nerves on "Keats and Nature" and "New Light" to determine their state as topics finished. There's a difference, but I couldn't predict the brevity or the length that will govern your choice.

PART I:

NATURE

CHAPTER ONE

Conversations on Nature

Causeries—easy talk—is better than *Conversations* for describing what I would do in the five "conversations" to follow; and *informalities* is getting close to the gist of the matter. For I have shunned textual specifics of author and title to champion overviews on nature's meaning and way with the Romantics, Keats, and the Victorians.

Naturally, in *Conversations,* one will find notes that plump and notes that augment. I do not dare do without them. You will not find, however, notes that burgeon with author, title, place of publication, publisher, date of publication, and pagination. I recognize my risk and the plan's audacity in such simplification. Nevertheless, I sense a need and feel a right to do what I have done. Plainly, *Conversations* is my last inclusion in *Ranges of Romanticism.* I would make of it my relaxation and therapy. Besides, as I know, and as you will, plenty of specifics and notes exist in "Keats and Nature" to compensate for their shortage here. Please, then, these facts: I am a scholar; I can write notes; I do repeat myself; I do not plagiarize others.

Welcome, then, to *Conversations on Nature;* written in 1989, read in November 1989, at the Arkansas Philological Association.

TMH

Conversation I

1750

1750. A good enough year to mark the advent of Rousseau and to anticipate Herder.[1] The two will transform nature into more

3

physical presence and less spiritual connotation.[2] To be sure, nature will retain much of its spiritual heritage after Rousseau and Herder, but it will also reflect in the two the beginnings of the end of a momentous brawl: the empiricists' conquest of the rationalists and the transcendentalists for the western mind.[3] Above all, nature will play host to a notion that has altered the thought-work of each of us since—namely, that energy, not love, is the motivating factor of the universe. Whether in man, animal, plant, or mineral, or whether mental or physical in manifestation, energy is the focus, the motivator, and the source of our growth, bloom,[4] change, and even evolution.[5]

Upon first glance, one may be tempted to conclude that the nature concepts to follow, with their divisions of Nature and Man and Nature and God, are not right-on with Romantics like Rousseau, Herder, Wordsworth, Shelley, and Keats. Rest in peace on that surmise. The concepts to follow provide ample base and perspective for the above Romantics plus all other Romantics in their great to-do about a great idea.

To the nature concepts I have added commentary with examples where I have thought them useful. But, always, I have reserved room in my mind for the readers' concepts and syntheses when such have seemed to them needed. At the end—after my "last words"—I hope that the reader will have concluded, as have I, that the nature ideas are effective, and represent, as I know, nature fundamentals beneath which no one as yet has gone deeper.

I would acknowledge my debt to the *Great Ideas II* (Edited by Mortimer Adler in *Great Books of the Western World*. Chicago: Encyclopedia Britannica, 1952, pp. 225-230) for the definitions with examples about to occur. The numbers in parentheses in the text refer to this work.

Nature and Man

1. *Products of nature* differ from works of art in that man in the latter has added something to nature (225).

Being said here is: Man may imitate nature, but cannot make a facsimile of it. Man embellishes nature with his ideas and products. These may borrow from nature so well as to seem natural. They are not; they are "works of art"—artifacts, products—having high usage and natural leanings.

4

2. *Nature as bad.* Hobbes and, after 1750, Kant and Hegel, declared a "state of nature" is a "state of war" (225). Locke disagreed. Nature, he said, is the base for "men living together according to reason" (225).

Thus, I shall add, Locke became the fundament on which Rousseau, Herder, and Schelling, and then Wordsworth, Coleridge, and Chateaubriand were to lean when treating nature. Keats, as we know, agreed and disagreed with Hobbes, Kant, and Hegel on nature.[6] Nature to Keats could be bad, but, if my reading of his poems and letters is accurate, was more good than bad.[7]

3. *Natural organizations.* The bee-hive and the ant-mound are constructs of a natural society; that is, they are made and inhabited not by man, but by nature's bee and ant (225).

Keats's *Hyperion,* then, or any other of his poems, including that effusion to nature "I stood tip-toe upon a little hill," may celebrate nature but is not "natural." Rather, the poem is a human construct, a work of art celebrating, say, nature as subject or a flow of line so smooth as to seem "natural."

4. *Natural.* Common to all meanings of the word is the notion that *natural* consists of what man has not "altered or enlarged" (226).

Example. Forests untouched are in natural state. Fenced in or housed, they have been embellished or changed by man from a natural state. They can, of course, still appear more natural than civilized, if the change is slight.

5. *Human nature.* It undergoes transformations through additions of knowledge and modifications of instincts and habits. "The sum of these changes constitutes what nurture has added to nature" (226).

Education, crises of love and hate, and habits of fitness can alter human nature. These facts would not be true of the ant or bee, both examples of inborn behavior.

6. *Cultures. Civilizations.* They represent contrasts to nature, however aligned to nature they may seem (226). Rousseau thought man had lost, not gained, by exchanging the natural for the civilized life (226).

This fact, then: The noble savage and the child of nature are not effects of nature. Rather, they lean toward nature as their ideal, and are closer to nature than the urbanite, the socialite, the philosopher, or the college professor.

7. *Human products.* They are in contrast to natural products like the bee-hive, bee honey, and the bee community (226); or to natural

effects like the storm, the wave, the lightning, or the dew—my additions. A human product is, then, the box enclosing the bee-hive or the dike repelling the wave. A human product derives from "learning, inventions, and civilizations." It is the consequence of man's reason and freedom (226).

8. *Aristotle.* The natural is that which is "by nature unchangeable and has everywhere the same force." For instance, "fire burns the same in Athens and in Persia" (227).

Simple judgment, accurate truth, ultimate insight.

9. *Natural and man-made.* To see their difference, compare the spider's web or the beaver's dam with a highway, a building, or a city. The former products are instinctive and uniform productions; the latter, variables of infinite degree, products of "human decision and choice" (227).

Nature and God

10. *Plato.* Things said to be made by nature are "works of divine art," made by God, who is outside of nature and the only uncreated being (228). By contrast, the Stoics saw God as inherent in visible nature, and nature as a work of art created by its own intrinsic spirit, Mother Nature (228).

11. *God's world.* Nature in God's world includes not only physical and sensible things, but also the spiritual world of angels and souls. Thus, the spiritual world is no more supernatural than bodies (228).

The thesis is Christian, especially Aquinian Christian.

12. *Spinoza.* He identifies nature with the infinite and eternal substance of God. Nature represents the "totality of finite things both material and immaterial"; but exceeds the totality since God, nature's creator, is greater than the sum of Nature's parts (229).

Cogent thinking that brought the 17th century closer to Nature, but deferred the century's decision to separate Nature from God until century's end with John Locke.

Last word. The emphasis on Nature and Man in the above concepts is fit evidence that, before Rousseau and Herder, a groundwork for associations of nature with man rather than with God was set for the arrival of Keats, Shelley, and Byron, as well as for Swinburne, Hugo, and Vigny. One cannot, of course, ever ignore

6

the evidence of Nature and God to be found in Novalis, Wordsworth, Coleridge, and Emerson. Still, today, 1989, one sees the latter poets as mystics at work on concepts outworn rather than prophetic, and entirely at a distance from the relationship we know best and applaud most, that of Nature and Science.

Seen therefore is this fact: Rousseau and Herder, and Keats and the English Romantics, were at work upon a nature that by 1750 had arrived midpoint in its man/nature and matter/spirit relationships. As such, the Romantics found nature a subject for soaring, personalized judgments which, however sound or unsound, were intended to be revolutionary and ultimate. Now, at 20th century's end, one sees these judgments as quaint when placed beside the interpretations of the scientist and the naturalist.

Will there be a return to the 1750 call-outs on nature? Of course not. Nor should there be. Rather, one should be concentrating on what mathematics and the scientific method have wrought to create a precise and objectified creature that I would define as *le nouveau nature*. I speak of the technologized nature as ultimate to us in our computerized state as the Romantics' concepts were to them. But, stand by for our nature's demise, also; for die it will when man learns that nature's master is not technology and cannot be so long as man's technology changes nature into classifications apart from man rather than celebrating, as did the Romantics, a chemistry in man's union with nature or nature's with man. That chemistry is yet present, but no longer weighed.[8]

Conversation II

Nature and the Romantics

Even a fool's glance at the Romantics' concepts of nature shows that they lack precision, objectivity, and system, so their decline before a system more precise and objective, the scientists', was predictable. Also, the Romantics' concepts are crowded with overlapping variants. Let me advise you about the variants. If Romantic in background, never omit one. The variants illustrate the potency of nature to the subjective Romantics; they illustrate the trust the Romantics put in the term.[1] After Rousseau and Herder, they could not conceive of a better way of setting to rights the central meanings to their life. After all, the Enlightenment had excised the necessity of religion and had projected the importance of reason until reason had fallen from being essential into being sterile chatter. Nature, then, had become not only *le nouveau,* but also, as a way of life, a necessity. What for Newton had been a means for explaining a universe now became a therapy to a western world groping for new values that would hold.

Thus, Keats's world, awaiting him to be born. Keats's reception of nature, as the poems and letters suggest, is more intense but less intellectual than Coleridge's or Shelley's, but it is as sincere as Byron's is vapid, and one comes away from his nature passages in both poems and letters with the conclusion that, just as in his dealings with friends, ideas, and causes, he meant what he had said.[2]

Conversation III

Nature in Keats's Poems

Nature was not an overwhelming topic to Keats in his poems. His concern for beauty, love, mankind, and self outweigh his concern for nature. Still, nature is everywhere in his poems as subject, solace, or simply atmosphere. Any reading of Keats will reveal how ready he was with an idea that the Romantics had adopted as major.

Still, the question remains: How deeply did Keats get into the nature-subject? The evidence suggests, whatever the elevation or the excess, rather more deep than less. Away he went in his nature-dance, from appeals 1) to sense and sensation, to 2) thought and idea; and from uplifts of 3) morality and therapy to 4) effects upon poet and reader. Perhaps too often his appeals are to sense and sensation; too seldom, I believe, to morality and idea; in bounty, however, the great chime, and irreducible prize, his effects upon poet and reader.

Never could one say that Keats had gone as passionately into nature as had Wordsworth, or as deeply as Coleridge and Shelley. Nevertheless, his awareness of nature is unchallengeable, and his expression as various and wondrous as Coleridge's or Wordsworth's.

8

One must allow for the fact that Keats arrived on the nature scene just as the Romantics were loosening their bond to nature that, before 1807,[1] could not have been understood by most Romantics, much less allowed.

Conversation IV

Nature in Keats's Letters

The nature passages are abundant in the earlier letters, but diminish in presence and significance in the later ones. In the earlier letters, one notes many literal descriptions of nature and many expressions of rapture in response to nature. Nature is not only physical but diverse. Sun, moon, birds, plants, weather; the mountains and valleys and the lakes and sea—these find their place in the letters. Naturally, they predict many a passage to be in the poems.

One's impression in the letters just as in the poems is that nature means less to Keats than people, and is less beautiful and perhaps less of a stimulus to his poetry. Beauty, people, love, classifications, and memoir are Keats's real subjects in the letters,[1] but one would notice the absence of his nature inclusions if they were not present. Let us say that Keats needed to think and to write about nature in order to fulfill his Age, even as his Age needed nature in order to supply its poets, including Keats, with something to say.

Conversation V

Nature and the Victorians

The Victorians emulate the Romantics' notions on nature, intensifying religion in nature through Hopkins, objectifying nature through Darwin and Hardy, then uglifying nature through this and that scientist, social scientist, and poet. The fact is that nature, in its positive imprint, is the subject of the 18th-century empiricist and the 18th- and the 19th-century Romantic. Indeed, they all but introduce the subject, give it dimensionality and power, then abandon it for what they had abandoned to find nature, namely, God, morality, science and society. What the Victorians acquire therefore is an idea on its way to supersession.

Still, nature, so artfully used by the scientist and so decoratively embellished by the poet, remains an *object d'interet* of the Victorians. In the absence of more to behold and in the presence of less, they held on to nature, intensified its peril, magnified its glory, diminished its practicality, and abolished its therapy. What they had by 1900 was a hull, with Wordsworth at its center providing hope, but with Hardy, Darwin, Spencer, and Huxley at its perimeter suggesting catastrophe. Not even Ruskin nor the painting Pre-Raphaelites[1] could hold up to the latter, and, as one knows, Wordsworth has not held up to Picasso, Eliot, and Pound.[2]

Endnotes

Conversation I. 1750

[1] Jean-Jacques Rousseau, 1712-1778, decidedly born and brought up by 1750, but not into nature until then. See Rousseau's *Discours sur l'origine . . . de l'inegalite* (1750) for his benediction of nature's noble savage. Johann Gottfried von Herder, 1744-1803, decidedly a whelp of six in 1750 but, by 1769, a *Sturm und Drang* observer of nature's effect on man; and, by 1770, so imbued as to convert Goethe to nature and Romanticism. See Herder's *Journal am Reise* (1769) and Goethe's *Gotz von Berlichingen* (1773) and *Die Lieden des jungen Werthers* (1774).

[2] Always in the great Nature dialogue, one must accept the Greeks' leaning on their gods and goddesses for explanations of nature, and the medievalists' leaning on God. By comparison, the Romantics seem physical about nature, until one thinks of the scientists' interpretations today. Scientists are intensely physical in their demands for demonstrable, even mathematical, evidence.

[3] The progression into more physical interpretations of nature is neither steady nor inevitable. The transcendentalists and the deists will hold out for spiritualized interpretations until well into the mid-nineteenth century. Still, the empiricists' demand for sensorials, the

rationalists' for clarity, and the utilitarians' for usefulness are to have their say in nudging the western mind into concern for the concrete fact. Rousseau and Herder reflect the first two of these influences in their interpretations of nature.

[4] *Growth and bloom.* Herder's description of the civilization as a living organism; like nature's tree, it goes through a cycle of growth, bloom, and, to effect a triad, decay.

[5] *Evolution.* Already a topic for discourse before 1800, and later to be both challenge and tease to 19th and 20th-century geneticists and environmentalists.

[6] Much more evidence on Keats's view of nature as good and bad to be found in "Keats and Nature." See Nature Idea No. 40 for his position and my subsequent remarks on nature's bad influence.

[7] Numerically, the evidence for nature as being good rather than bad is overwhelming in Keats's concepts. Qualitatively, the imbalance is less patent. Nature as ugly, horrible, and vicious, Idea No. 38, in "Keats and Nature," nullifies at least a dozen concepts of nature as good.

[8] Prediction. Our rejection of the Romantics' concept of nature and acceptance of the scientists' and the naturalists' should become the anomaly of the 21st century. Not that the Romantics were so right in their concepts, but that the scientists and naturalists are so limited.

Conversation II: Nature and the Romantics

[1] "Variants on nature." Account for them also as evidence of nature become everyone's grist—a rights-of-man topic permitting repetitive detail and, sometimes, unapproachable vagueness. Stand by for another mention of variants in the introduction to "Keats and Nature."

[2] By 1878, Matthew Arnold had come to appreciate Keats's seriousness with ideas and causes and his decency with friends. The judgment has been so endorsed by subsequent critics and biographers that to mention it now would seem like a plagiarism. Yet, the fact is irreducible. Read Keats's poems and letters—not his critics and biographers—and find out for yourself.

Conversation III: Nature in Keats's Poems

[1] "1807." The date, so definite in statement, is elusive in application. One could have as easily singled out 1805 as the critical

11

year of the Romantics' turn away from nature; or, one could single out a year of the French or of the Germans in the 1830's or the 1840's. Still, to the extent that Wordsworth rather than Hugo, Baudelaire, or Heine is the crucial influence upon the subject, I suggest that Wordsworth's turn away from nature in 1807 (or 1805) is the year in which the turn has become irrevocable.

Conversation IV: Nature in Keats's Letters

[1] The overlapping of Keats's subjects in his letters with those in his poems is inevitable and irreproachable. Typically, the sequence is this: first, in the letters; then, in the poems. Same subject, differing language. In a sense, Keats's letters are his notebooks, of which he did not retain a copy for his poetic purpose.

Conversation V: Nature and the Victorians

[1] "Ruskin and the painting of the Pre-Raphaelites." Idealists of nature at first, but waning supporters before the social needs and aesthetic attractions of the Age.

[2] Picasso's cubism and expressionism represent a contradiction of nature; Eliot's and Pound's strictures on what to write and to appreciate in poetry have ravaged the nature interests of the Romantics, including Wordsworth's, Shelley's, and Keats's.

CHAPTER TWO

Keats and Nature

I would be rude, repetitious, and incorrect to tell you that "Keats and Nature" is just another annotation of nature ideas; or, another proof that Keats, Romantic, belonged to his Age; or, another assurance that his nature ideas are right-on with Goethe's, Wordsworth's, Coleridge's, and Shelley's. These facts, of course, do obtain in "Keats and Nature," but I trust that the facts have not intruded upon a more sensitive intention of the study, for I would evidence to you that Keats's concepts of nature in his letters and poems display an organic unity at variance with the fact that they, being Romantic, must illustrate the dispersion, break-up, and discontinuity commonly associated with Romanticism.

To be sure, the organic unity I speak of is not sustained from idea to idea among the nature concepts. Rather, it shows forth here and there in clusters of facts that not only relate but predict that certain ideas will follow if one in the cluster occurs. This fact is too assuring for me not to suggest therefore that Keats's concepts of nature reveal, if not system, nevertheless a commonalty that gathers and rounds into a Keatsian totality, making sense from beginning to end.

I am impressed with the variants at work in Keats's nature concepts. They are frequent and, being repetitive, they should paralyze the concepts. Actually, they occur to good purpose. For the variants reveal less a slipshod amble in and about a great idea than the potency of that idea to express, then re-express, itself in many ways. Both nature and man are the subject of these nature variants. I have attempted unexceptionally to make plain that fact as the variants appear in this study. I hope I have not omitted a single one.

13

Naturally, I have tried to introduce some order into Keats's nature concepts when the concepts did not merge by recognition. Nature as both good and bad, then, has been one compelling division; nature's metaphysics—yes, Keats can be metaphysical—has been another; characteristics of nature has been another; and, less numerous but more important, nature's influences and effects on man have been yet another. Frequently, a characteristic like *naturgefuhl*—nature-feeling—or nature's stimulation of man shows up as not only a characteristic, but also a segment in nature's metaphysics and nature's effect on man. Such instances confirm my thesis that an organic unity is seminal among the concepts. They reveal as well the fact that the concepts in their progression are circular in pattern rather than linear.

If these relationships of nature represent what I regard as the important contribution in the list to follow, I should not close without mention that the nature seen by Keats displays the traditional division of matter and spirit prominent since Plato. In this instance, more emphasis exists on a material nature than on a spiritual. But enough of a spiritual nature remains for the concepts to represent, as I have mentioned in "Conversations on Nature," a historical midpoint between the first concepts of the Greeks, more spiritual than physical, and those of today's scientists more physical than Keats or any other Romantic could have envisioned.[1]

Two last facts about "Keats and Nature." One, I have included without, I hope, disruption of context, a serendipity—the Victorian afterflow in Keats's nature concepts. As we know, the Victorians, after 1850, were fond of Keats. It should interest one to know that the Victorians, especially the critics, were also fond of his nature concepts—so fond, in fact, that they even wrote about them. I am saying, then, that the Victorians profile the fullest consensus on Keats's nature concepts that we have today. For this fact I refer you to the source to which I have gone, my *Keats and the Critics 1848-1900* (Salzburg: Universitat Salzburg, 1972).

Two, I am impressed with the way Keats has blended nature into man and man into nature in variants of parallel meaning. The parallelism assumes, I believe, the Rousseauan sentiments that man can be a man of nature, hence a natural in nature, or even, himself, a spot of nature. Already, in "Conversations on Nature," I have committed myself to the proposition that this Rousseauan sentiment is absurd; that, indeed, man can only approach being a natural in nature. Man, even the most primitive, with his freedom of choice

14

and capacity to reason, is ever beyond nature in his actions and interpretations. Nature is instinctual; its causes and effects are rigid and predictable. Man, even the man of nature, is ever rousted out of his instincts by an ability to be creative beyond predictable results.

In his poems and letters, Keats assumes this ability of man to become a projection of nature. The fact does not lessen the viability of most of his assumptions on nature and lessens not at all the impact of his nature poems and referents. Still, the fact does point a warning which Keats and the Romantics did not heed and which, today, we in our removal from nature except via television and computer may understand too little to challenge.

For the content of Keats's poems quoted in "Keats and Nature," I have gone to *The Poems of John Keats,* edited with introduction by Ernest De Selincourt (London: Methuen, 1905). For verification of dates, punctuation, long titles and short, and capitalized and lower-case lettering, I have set the De Selincourt edition alongside the H.W. Garrod edition *(The Poetical Works of John Keats.* Oxford: Clarendon Press, 1939), the Miriam Allott edition *(The Poems of John Keats.* London: Longman, 1970), and, especially, the Jack Stillinger edition *(The Poems of John Keats.* Cambridge: The Belknap Press of Harvard Univ. Press, 1978). For Keats's letters, I have gone to *The Letters of John Keats.* Edited by Huder Edward Rollins (Cambridge: Harvard Univ. Press, 1958. 2 volumes). My gratitude for these scrupulous assemblages of Keats is profound.

For orientation into Keats's nature concepts, I have leaned most upon Joseph Warren Beach, *Concepts of Nature in the Nineteenth Century.* New York: Macmillan (1936); and A.O. Lovejoy, "Nature as an Aesthetic Norm," *Essays in the History of Ideas.* Baltimore: Johns Hopkins Press, 1941; but relevantly upon Emery Neff, "Nature," *A Revolution in European Poetry.* New York: Columbia Univ. Press (1940). I could not close however without mention of a fourth resource that has embellished the other three. I refer to Norman Dacey, *Wordsworth's View of Nature and Its Ethical Consequences.* Cambridge: University Press (1948).

I. Nature's Positives

A. Nature Metaphysics

Idea 1. The cosmical unity of plants, animals, and man.

The idea, trimmed to Romantic specification, is Johann Gottfried Herder's (1744-1803).[1] Keats made no mention in letter or poem of Herder's theory, yet required of himself the empathic understanding that the theory predicts. In the letter to George and Georgianna Keats, February-May, 1819, he observes:

> The greater part of Man makes their way with the same instinctiveness, the same unwandering eye from their purposes, the same animal eagerness as the Hawk—The Hawk wants a mate, so does the Man— . . . They both want a nest and they both set about one in the same manner— . . . [2]

The letter sums up a relationship that Wordsworth and Coleridge understood even better than Keats, and that Goethe expressed in *Eins und Alles* (1821), "One and All."

The cosmical unity of plants, animals, and man represents the large nature view to which nature's communion with man, Idea 2, is the abbreviation. The opposite of the large view is the broken chain of being among plants, animals, and man.[3] Keats accepted the three views, and, in using them, illustrated his aesthetic of "negative capability," a poet's disinterested reach for material into sources both good and evil.

Still, a realistic caution from Keats appears in the same letter to George and Georgianna Keats. Disinterestedness, said Keats, cannot be

> pushed to an extremity—for in wild nature the Hawk would lose his Breakfast of Robins and the Robin his of worms. The lion must starve as well as the swallow—(Rollins, ed. *Letters,* II, 79).

The correction amends Keats's aesthetic on tolerance of subjects in poetry, but it does not undermine what Keats saw going on among plants, animals, and man.

Idea 2. Nature's communion with man, man's communion with nature.

Another cosmical layout, this one simpler to read and envisage, but no less difficult to apply.

16

Coleridge made man's communion with nature an attribute of Shakespeare,[4] and Shelley of the poet with imagination.[5] Keats, truly Shakespearian and imaginative, records the idea early and late in his letters. Thus, to Benjamin Bailey, 22 November 1817:

> The setting sun will always set me to rights—or if a Sparrow come before my Window I take part in its existence and pick about the gravel . . . (Rollins, ed. *Letters*, I, 186).

And to Fanny Brawn, 24 (?) February 1820:

> Do you hear the Th(rush) singing over the field? I think it is a sign of mild weather—so much the better for me. Like all sinners now I am ill I philosophise aye out of my attachment to everything. Trees, flowers, thrushes Sp(ring), Summer, Claret, etc. . . . (Rollins, ed., *Letters*, II, 265).[6]

These letters express better than those of Idea 1 Keats's notion of "negative capability" found in the Shakespearian poet. The idea itself, nature's communion with man, man's with nature, was not picked up by either Romantic or Victorian critics of Keats but has been a concern of Keatsians since Ernest De Selincourt, 1905.[7] Said De Selincourt:

> Man, Keats would imply, is himself a part of Nature, only to be distinguished from Nature in his self-consciousness and in his . . . recognition of beauty . . . in Nature, whilst poetry is [his] expression of . . . kinship. It is on this relationship with Nature that the . . . appeal of poetry . . . rests, whilst the similar effect produced upon us by . . . Nature and . . . poetry is (because) each is a . . . manifestation of the same idea. The true poet . . . is instinctively guided by Nature to (poetry) . . . to clothe his conception as much as he is inspired by Nature with the conception . . . he desires to clothe.[8]

De Selincourt had found Keats's identification with nature stated in *Sleep and Poetry*. Here, he adds, Keats expressed two ideas,

> [one] that a full communion with Nature and an understanding of her . . . beauty is only possible after a sympathetic study of human nature . . .; and [two], that

17

after a contemplation of the ideal as revealed by Nature
the sordid realities of life are felt all the more keenly, and
would be intolerable, were it not for the sustaining power
of the imagination which keeps alive the ideal within the
poet's heart and saves him from despair (De Selincourt
407).

Keats shared a reaction against nature just as he shared a rapport
with her. His sentiments do not repudiate nature, but do observe an
impersonal side that Leopardi, Tennyson, Leconte de Lisle,
Baudelaire, and Arnold were to see in their decades of the nineteenth
century.[9]

For Keats's rapport, or communion, with nature, see "Where's
the Poet?" (1818):

> Where's the Poet? Show him! Show him!
> Muses nine! that I may know him! . . .
> 'Tis the man who with a bird,
> Wren or Eagle, finds his way to
> All its instincts;—he hath heard
> The Lion's roaring, and can tell
> What his horny throat expresseth;
> And to him the tiger's yell
> Comes articulate, and presseth
> On his ear like mother-tongue.
>
> ll. 1-2, 8-15.

Other instances of Keats's rapport are in "I stood tip-toe upon
a little hill" (1816), *Endymion* (1817), and *Sleep and Poetry* (1816).

Idea 3. Nature-feeling *(Naturgefuhl)*[10]

An end-of-the-line feeling for nature by man, and a necessary
evidence of man's cosmical relationship with plants and animals. If
a crucial phase in any metaphysics of nature, nature-feeling also exists
as both characteristic of nature and influence. As a characteristic, it
signifies man's devotion to nature; as the influence, it explains the
reason for man's devotion.

Nature-feeling—*naturgefuhl*—is Arthur O. Lovejoy's way of
describing the "in-feeling"—*Einfuhlung*—that characterizes man's
communion with nature. Typically, *joy* is the "in-feeling" man gets
from being with nature; the feeling is implicit as well in nature's
stimulation of man, Idea 8.

18

Evidences of *joy* may be found in Keats's "How many bards" (1816), "I stood tip-toe" (1816), *Sleep and Poetry* (1816), "On the Sea" (1817), *Endymion* (1817), and "Hence burgundy, claret and port" (1818). For three more instances, see "There is a joy in footing slow across a silent plain" (1818), *Lamia* (1819), and "Ode on Melancholy" (1819).

Nature-feeling also has a panic side from its storms, avalanches, droughts, and human wreckage. Keats sensed this prospect in man's communings with nature. For how well, see Nature envisioned as ugly, horrible, and vicious, Idea 38.

Nature-feeling (*naturgefuhl*) represents a major idea in the nature canon of Keats, even as it did in the young Wordsworth, and in Byron and Shelley. A uniqueness of nature-feeling in an age ambiguous about nature was that the feeling is only man's, not nature's.

Examples:

> Thee I must praise above all other glories
> That smile us on to tell delightful stories.
> For what has made the sage or poet write
> But the fair paradise of Nature's light.
>
> "I stood tip-toe," ll. 123-126

> ...[F]ine sounds are floating wild
> About the earth: happy are ye and glad.
>
> *Sleep and Poetry,* ll. 228-229

> Oh ye who have your eyeballs vex'd and tir'd,
> Feast them upon the wideness of the sea;
> Oh ye whose ears are dinned with uproar rude,
> Or fed too much with cloying melody—
> Sit ye near some old cavern's mouth and brood
> Until ye start, as if the sea-nymphs quired.
>
> "On the Sea," ll. 9-14

> Instead of a pitiful rummer,
> My wine overbrims a whole summer
> My bowl is the sky,
> And I drink at my eye,
> Till I feel in the brain
> A Delphian pain—
>
> "Hence burgundy, claret and port," ll. 5-10[11]

Idea 4. Nature as visible thought; thought as invisible nature.[12]

Kant and Schelling accepted this nature relationship; Goethe includes the idea in early nature writings; in *Sartor Resartus* (1833-4), Carlyle cites the relationship as a "natural emblem." Coleridge had accepted the idea by 1796; Wordsworth, no later than 1805. After 1807, the idea splits into two directions as (1) transcendental theology adopted by Coleridge, Emerson and Carlyle, and (2) as naturalistic utterance adopted by Wordsworth. To Wordsworth, the spirit of nature is a "shaping faculty" of man. To Coleridge in 1802, it is evidence of a higher spiritual law, interpretable by man.[13]

Keats received no credit from the nineteenth century for seeing nature as visible thought, and thought as invisible nature. Indeed, the Victorians made clear the fact that, among the Romantic poets, the idea was not Keats's, but Coleridge's or Wordsworth's. Nevertheless, the idea does occur in Keats's nature poetry. I cite you *Sleep and Poetry* (1816).

> It (the Sun) has a glory, and naught else can share it:
> The thought thereof is awful, sweet, and holy,
> Chasing away all worldliness and folly;
> Coming sometimes like fearful claps of thunder,
> Or the low rumblings earth's regions under;
> And sometimes like a gentle whispering
> Of all the secrets of some wond'rous thing
> That breathes about us in the vacant air. . . .
>
> ll. 24-31

Idea 5. Nature as a Platonic idea, if imperfectly realized; nature as *la belle nature* rendered into type (Lovejoy 71).

Nature as Platonic? Consider *spiritual, mythic,* or *personified* as equivalents along with intimations of a perfect nature suggested by its earthbound instance. Nature as *la belle nature*? Consider *beautiful, idyllic,* or perhaps *archetypal* as equivalents and hope for no overlapping with Platonic.

The two notions project nature as ideal, and, despite the fact that evidence for them is lacking in Keats's letters, his poems are crowded with examples. A common thread in the notions is that nature in its material forms reflects a spiritual state that is endurably beautiful as in *la belle nature,* and endurably true and good as in nature Platonized.

20

The Romantics did not delve into Keats's poetry for Platonic treasure, but, by 1880, the Victorians had—first, in Frances M. Owen's *John Keats: A Study* (1876);[14] then, ten years later, in Roden Noel's interpretation of *Hyperion.*[15] Other Victorians adopted both *Endymion* and *Hyperion* as examples of "Greek nature," "Greek personification of nature," and "Greek natural myth." To one initiated into Greek thought, these epithets connote nature as Platonized or as representing a Grecian ideal that, to 18th-century France, became *la belle nature.*[16]

Considering Keats's approach in "Ode on a Grecian Urn" (1819), one should not be surprised to find these idealized states showing up in "Ode to Psyche" (1819) and "Ode on Melancholy" (1819); also in "I stood tip-toe" (1816), "Bards of passion and of mirth" (1818), *Lamia* (1819), the *Fall of Hyperion* (1819), and, as mentioned, *Endymion* (1817) and *Hyperion* (1818-1819).

Examples:

Nature as Platonic ideal:

> Bards of passion and of mirth,
> Ye have left your souls on earth!
> Have ye souls in heaven too,
> Double-lived in regions new?
> Yes, and these of heaven commune
> With the spheres of sun and moon;
> With the noise of fountains wond'rous,
> And the parle of voices thund'rous. . . .
> > "Bards of passion and of mirth," 11. 1-8

Nature as *la belle nature*

> Queen of the wide air; thou most lovely queen
> Of all the brightness that mine eyes have seen!
> As though exceedest all things in thy shine,
> So every tale, does this sweet tale of thine.
> O for three words of honey, that I might
> Tell but one wonder of thy bridal night!
> > "I stood tip-toe," 11. 205-210

Nature as an ambiguous *la belle nature* in *Lamia:*

> [Lamia] was a gordian shape of dazzling hue,
> Vermilion-spotted, golden, green, and blue;
> Striped like a zebra, freckled like a pard,

21

Eyed like a peacock, and all crimson barr'd;
And full of silver moons, that, as she breathed,
Dissolv'd, or brighter shone, or interwreathed
Their lusters with the gloomier tapestries—

I, 47-53

Nature Platonized (and personified) in *Lamia:*

Upon a time, before the faery broods
Drove Nymph and Satyr from the Prosperous woods,
Before King Oberon's bright diadem,
Sceptre, and mantle, clasp'ed with dewy gem,
Frighted away the Dryads and the Fauns
From rushes green, and brakes, and cowslip'd lawns,
The ever-smitten Hermes empty left
His golden throne, bent warm on amorous theft: . . .

I, 1-8

Amid all the gristle and grist invading talk on nature's metaphysical properties, one must see in nature's garb as Platonic ideal and as *la belle nature* a climactic quest for getting nature set. By comparison, the cosmical unity of plants, animals, and man represents first gropings toward a first view. In nature as Platonic idea and as *la belle nature,* the quest is over; the insight, found; and a permanence, assured. What has occurred is the uplift from a nature embodied in physical show to a nature still physical, but perceived to have proportion, unity, and form. Rejected in the process are concepts based on matter, sensation, and speculation; accepted is the reasoned recognition of a nature committed to become flawless; to be, then, true, good, and beautiful.[17] To have read *Endymion, Hyperion,* and even *Lamia* without this understanding is to have missed Keats's way of loading nature with some of his finest rifts of ore.

B. Nature Characteristics: *Natura Naturans* and *Natura Naturata*

Nature characteristics? After dozens of them, one can conclude that, to the Romantics, nature was natural, free, rural, and felt; also, sacred, evolved, benevolent, and real. I have retreated to Spinoza for organizing such an array. I have picked up his terms, *natura naturans* (L., pres. part.) and *natura naturata* (L., past part.), ignored his use for describing a natural universe, then shaped them into meanings of my own.

Natura naturans means "nature 'naturing' "; in my sense, nature creating, generating, or expressing characteristics in their budding stage. *Natura naturata,* on the other hand, means "nature 'natured'"; that is, nature created, generated, evidenced, and enriched beyond its particular state to describe patterns of influence and effect.[18]

I like the terms; I like my meanings despite recognizing that the meanings may cause comment and that neither nature "naturing" nor nature "natured" will get one all the way into nature's characteristics. Still, as beacons, they hold up in illustrating what nature could mean to Keats, the Romantics, and the Victorians.

C. Characteristics. *Natura Naturans*

Idea 6. Nature has a life of its own.

An all-important characteristic. Without it one should not assume nature's role as an example for mankind. The characteristic implies that nature is neither man's subject nor reflection, neither God's pawn nor paradigm. It does imply that nature is *sui generis,* with its own activity, presence, and pace. Nature having its own life permits nature to exceed man, to become greater in size, and vaster in scope. It permits nature to have the latitude, influence, and effect that the Romantics accepted. Thus, what had become an all-embracing physical system to Newton has become, less than a century later, a refuge, precedent, and authority to Rousseau.

The implication in Nature's having a life of its own is that nature is free rather than represents freedom. The view is post-Rousseauan, but not post-Romantic. Paradoxically, neither early nor late Romantics, but a middle Victorian, John Ruskin, became the idea's significant sponsor.

Ruskin, in attacking the Romantic's tendency to humanize nature,[19] ignored the undoubted communion and communication that can exist between nature and man. Nevertheless, his argument that nature should not be humanized became a welkin for Victorians ready to drop their Romantic coil. Tennyson anguished over the impasse in *In Memoriam* (1850); Arnold said Nature is not benevolent, but "cruel," "stubborn," and "fickle";[20] the Pre-Raphaelites made an interest in nature secondary to an interest in legend, literature, and art.[21] Nature is unconcerned with man, said Vigny in "La Maison des Bergers" (1844). The view is Darwin's and Maxwell's in their

23

recognition that a scientist works best with a nature objectified and impersonalized.

Ruskin, despite serious regard for Keats, missed the poet's acceptance of nature's independence expressed in "To My Brother George" (1816) and in "I stood tip-toe" (1816). There the judgment is, nevertheless. Examples follow.

> Many the wonders I this day have seen: . . .
> The ocean with its vastness, its blue green,
>   Its ships, its rocks, its caves, its hopes, its fears.—
>   Its voice mysterious, which whoso hears
> Must think on what will be, and what has been.
> "To My Brother George," ll. 1, 5-8

> And watch intently Nature's gentle doings:
> They will be found softer than ring-dove's cooings.
> How silent comes the water round that bend;
> Not the minutest whispers does it send
> To the o'erhanging sallows: blades of grass
> Slowly across the chequer'd shadows pass.
> "I stood tip-toe," ll. 63-68.

Idea 7. Nature as literal description.

Nature as literal description: inconsequential as a characteristic, but emphatic in Keats's poetry. Keats is being literal when describing the Southampton landscape to George and Tom Keats, 15 April 1817: ". . . Brown furze . . ., lopped trees, cow ruminating—ditto Donkey" (Rollins, ed. *Letters,* I, 128). In a letter to Reynolds, on the 17th and 18th of April 1817, he notes:

> I . . . have found several delightful wood-alleys, and copses, and quick freshes— As for primroses—the Island (Wight) ought to be called Primrose Island: that is, if the notion of Cowslips agree thereto . . . (Rollins, ed. *Letters,* I, 131).

Yet another literal description, but with more thought and plan, appears in the letter to Benjamin Bailey, 13 March 1818: "Things-real," wrote Keats, include the sun, moon and stars along with "passages of Shakespeare." "Things seminal" include the clouds as well as love (Rollins, ed. *Letters,* I, 243).

24

Keats's literal landscapes were especially observed by Victorians citing Keats as a natural poet. Lovejoy, always thoughtful, but sometimes ponderous, sees nature description as an "adherence to probability," but distinguishes it from "verisimilitude, the adherence to apparent or supposed probability" (Lovejoy 74). The Victorian critics made no such fine-point in reading Keats. Rather, Keats was, simply, a poet of nature.

Gilfillan, Shairp, Scherer, Colvin, Palgrave, and Downer recognized the literal descriptions in Keats's nature poetry,[22] but were more engrossed with the natural beauty of his lines. A major poem "To Autumn" fulfills a literal description of nature, but Victorians, late enough in their appreciation of the poem, had complicated Keats too well as Pre-Raphaelite or Grecian to see "To Autumn" as simple depiction. Bridges, for instance, lauded the poem as an expression of the Greek classical spirit.[23] "To Autumn" is, of course, also that.

The early and middle Victorians could have grasped better the literal character of Keats's nature descriptions had his early way of writing a poem possessed less language and more message and plot. Still, late Victorians Colvin and Downer envisaged "To Autumn" as existing for its own sake. In the twentieth century, Emery Neff has made a similar observation (Colvin, 57; Downer, 10; Neff, *Rev.,* 188).

Literal descriptions of nature occur in "O Solitude! if I must with thee dwell" (1816), "I stood tip-toe" (1816), "On the Grasshopper and Cricket" (1816), "On the Sea" (1817), "Epistle to J.H. Reynolds" (1818), and "To Ailsa Rock" (1818); also, in *The Eve of St. Agnes* (1819), "The Eve of St. Mark" (1819), "Ode to a Nightingale" (1819), and, as said, "To Autumn" (1819). Obviously, the concept is a leading nature-expression by Keats. Examples:

> When all the birds are faint with the hot sun,
>   And hide in cooling trees, a voice will run
> from hedge to hedge about the new-mown mead;
>   That is the Grasshopper's—he takes the lead
>   In summer luxury,—he has never done
>   With his delights; . . .
>   "On the Grasshopper and Cricket," ll. 2-7

The owl, for all his feathers, was a-cold;
The hare limp'd trembling through the frozen grass,
And silent was the flock in woolly fold. . . .
                    The Eve of St. Agnes, ll. 2-4

The city streets were clean and fair
From wholesome drench of April rains,
And on the western window panes,
The chilly sunset faintly told
Of unmature'd green vallies cold, . . .
                    The Eve of St. Mark, ll. 4-8

The grass, the thicket, and the fruit-tree wild;
    White hawthorn, and the pastoral eglantine;
        Fast-fading violets cover'd up in leaves; . . .
    The coming musk-rose, full of dewy wine,
        The murmurous haunt of flies on summer eves.
                "Ode to a Nightingale," ll. 45-47, 49-50

Then, "To Autumn," first as literal description:

Season of mists and mellow fruitfulness,
    Close bosom-friend of the naturing sun;
Conspiring with him how to load and bless
    With fruit the vines that round the thatch-
    eves run; . . .

                                        ll. 1-4

Then, same stanza, nature, enriched, a "thing of beauty," Idea 21:

To bend with apples the moss'd cottage trees,
    And fill all fruit with ripeness to the core;
        To swell the gourd, and plump the hazel shells
    With a sweet kernel; to set budding more,
And still more, later flowers for the bees,
Until they think warm days will never cease,
    For summer has o'er-brimm'd their clammy cells.
                                        ll. 5-11

Two more stanzas and "To Autumn" has become a "thing of beauty" so replete that one can no longer receive it as only literal description.

Keats's literal descriptions find the poet working easily in

26

nature—on the ground floor, amid transformations of landscape into metonymy, metaphor, and personification. The descriptions, as the examples show, occur throughout his career, but the instances are more numerous earlier, when the poet had less to say, than later, when he had more than he had time to say it.

I repeat: In the beginning, Keats's literal descriptions of nature are emphatic, but more from vividness of word than from tightness of plot. They represent what most poets create at first start. Appropriate, then, is the idea's place, at the beginning of *Characteristics,* just as more meaningful nature characteristics occur later. It will not follow that the more meaningful nature characteristics will be found in the more meaningful poems. Characteristics do not work that way, nor does a poet's brain. Characteristics will show up here and there, but will profit most within poems having not only plot but depth and magnitude. The perfect example of this is not *The Eve of St. Agnes* or "The Eve of St. Mark," but the "Ode to a Nightingale."

Idea 8. Nature, a stimulant of the senses.

A Romantic familiar adopted by the Victorians regarding Wordsworth as well as Keats. Said Keats to Benjamin Bailey, 18, 22 July 1818:

> I should not have consented to myself these four Months tramping in the highlands but that I thought it would give me more experience, . . . identify finer scenes, load me with grander Mountains, . . . than would stopping at home among Books, even though I should read Homer— . . . (Rollins, ed. *Letters,* I, 342).

To C. W. Dilke, 22 September 1819:

> Talking of pleasure, this moment I was. . . holding to my Mouth a Nectarine. . . . It went down soft, pulpy, slushy, oozy—all its delicious embonpoint melted down my throat like a large beautiful strawberry (Rollins, ed. *Letters,* II, 179).

In both letters, nature stimulates Keats just as, with other results, it has stimulated Wordsworth waiting in "wise passiveness."[24] Swinburne, Masson, Sherer, Colvin, Stoddard, and Bridges see Keats stimulated by nature.[25] The idea, related to Keats, is primary among the Victorians from 1845 to 1880.

One finds nature "naturing" the senses in "How many bards gild the lapses of time" (1816), *Sleep and Poetry* (1816), "On *The Story of Rimini,*" (1817), *Endymion* (1817), and the *Fall of Hyperion* (1819).

> So the unnumber'd sounds that evening store;
>   The song of birds—the whispering of the leaves—
>   The voice of waters—the great bell that heaves
> With solemn sound, —and thousands others more,
>   That distance of recognizance bereaves,
> Make pleasing music, and not wild uproar.
>
> "How many bards . . .," ll. 9-14

I should add that "How many bards" applies also to Nature's originality and continuous evolution of insights and novelty (Lovejoy, 75, Idea 10.

Another instance of nature as a stimulant of the senses:

> First the realm I'll pass
> Of Flora, and old Pan: sleep in the grass,
> Feed upon apples red, and strawberries,
> And choose each pleasure that my fancy sees. . . .
>
> *Sleep and Poetry,* ll. 101-104

At the end of the line from nature as a stimulant of the senses is nature become an effect of beauty to the viewer, or an inspiration arousing his love. As a felt experience, nature afforded Keats the choice of becoming a poet of sensations. As imprints inspiring beauty and love, nature afforded Keats the choice of becoming an ultimate poet. As it turned out, Keats became both poets, but with the proviso that his choice of beauty and love would be no more moral than his choice of sensations would be but descriptive. Thus, Keats in three phases of nature appreciation.

Nature as a stimulant of the senses is a major description of Keats's poems until 1880; it becomes less noted thereafter until it almost disappears as a Keatsian attribute in the 1930's. Still, no one has challenged Keats's right to respond to nature as he did, nor will they. The letter, a repetition of footnote 6's, may explain why.

To J. H. Reynolds, 21 September 1819:

How beautiful the season is now—How fine the air. A

temperate sharpness about it. Really, without joking, chaste weather—Dian skies—I've never liked stubble fields so much as now—Aye better than the chilly green of the spring. Somehow a stubble plain looks warm—in the same way that some pictures look warm . . . (Rollins, ed. *Letters,* II, 167).

Idea 9. Nature-feeling *(naturgefuhl)*

Naturgefuhl. First of all, it is the response to nature's stimulation of the senses, therefore entitled to be a characteristic as well as a phase in Nature Metaphysics, Sec. I, Idea 3. But what is the response? In its implication, the meaning wavers. I judge that nature-feeling can be generated as state of being, mood, or emotion; can lead to slightest arousal or to deepest trauma. I have indicated in Idea 3 that *joy* is the special arousal in Keats's encounter with nature, but one cannot ignore motivations of pity and sympathy in both "Ode to a Nightingale" (1819) and "Ode to Melancholy" (1819), nor of fear and foreboding in the "Epistle to J.H. Reynolds" (1818). My belief is that, while granting *naturgefuhl* its state as a nature characteristic, it goes better as a phase in nature metaphysics.

See Idea 3 for copious examples of nature-feeling *(naturgefuhl).* They can be translated into either feelings of the poet or responses of the reader. But required for the reader is his integration of the example with the poem as a whole.

Idea 10. Nature (representing to man) originality, novelty, and revolution of insights (Lovejoy 75).

I do not find these notions of nature in either Keats's poems or letters. I have found, however, two critics of Victorian heritage who discuss Keats's poems thus: Richard Henry Stoddard and Edmund Scherer.[26] The Romantics critics did not find the parallel in Keats, nor did Keats seem to have had the notion.

In Idea 12, a reshaping of the above idea emphasizes nature's role in man's originality and freedom from "reflective design." This is the characteristic the Victorians pursued in assessing Keats as a poet of "natural genius." In making the appraisal, the Victorians took into consideration Keats's re-creation of Greek myth and romance and his original insights on beauty in nature.

The Victorians' reference to Keats's "natural endowment" was also Kant's way of assessing genius.[27] It became an ultimate way of celebrating Keats well into the first quarter of the twentieth century, when explications replaced personalia, and the ideas and style of Keats's poetry became of more moment than Keats's long tromp over, say, the hills and glens of the Highlands.

Idea 11. Nature representing (to man) a freedom from rules; an irregularity and asymmetry; a self-expression and disregard of precedents (Lovejoy 72, 74)

For variants of this cluster of characteristics, see Idea 12, Nature revealed in man's feeling at the expense of his intellect and in his freedom from reflective design; see also Idea 10, Nature representing (to man) originality and novelty.

More Romantics and Victorians found nature's freedom from rules and irregularity unsatisfactorily illustrated in *Endymion.* Nature's self-expression and disregard of precedents they transferred into eulogies of Keats's originality. Kant argued in the *Critique of Judgment* on the right of poetic genius to be original and self-expressive (Kant 525). Keats has approached Kant's position in saying that poetry should come as naturally as leaves on a tree.

An instance of freedom from rules occurs in "What the Thrush Said . . ."

> O fret not after knowledge! I have none,
> And yet my song comes native with the warmth.
> O fret not after knowledge! I have none,
> And yet the evening listens.

11. 9-12

(Of course, this may or may not be a Keats poem. De Selincourt includes it, but Garrod, Allott, and Stillinger do not. The poem may have been retitled, as so many titles have been in the Allott and Stillinger editions.)

Idea 12. Nature, revealed in man's feeling at the expense of his intellect; in his freedom from reflective design; and in his joy in nature (Lovejoy 74).

Lovejoy's findings reveal nature as an influence on man *(naturata).* They reveal what happens in man's communion with nature, Idea 2; and in his joy over nature, they get to the source of man's nature-feeling, Idea 3. The Victorian critics connected these nature-roles to Keats.[28] The notions were instrumental, also, in

Colvin's and Downer's conclusions, already mentioned, that Keats loved nature for her own sake. Variants in the above nature-roles are Nature as a stimulant of the senses, Idea 8; and Nature representing a freedom from rules, a disregard of precedents, and a self-expression, Idea 11. An illustration from Keats occurs in "On Visiting the Tomb of Burns" (1818).

> The town, the churchyard, and the setting sun,
>   The clouds, the trees, the rounded hills all seem,
>   Though beautiful, cold—strange—as in a dream,
> I dreamed long ago, now new begun, . . .
>
> ll. 1-4

Another is in "What the Thrush Said" (1818). See the preceding characteristic, Idea 11, for the "Thrush" illustration.

Idea 13. Nature as an evolutionary process.

This "egghead" insight on nature could be located under Nature Metaphysics, Section I, Ideas 1-5, if one allowed for all the implications suggested of a nature in evolution. Still, the idea finds closer identification as a characteristic ever generating, ever "becoming" within its nature context, and ever illustrating in miniature a "growth, bloom, and decay" that Herder assigned to civilizations.[29] Always change, always evolution. What Charles Darwin was to render into a system, the Romantics—Goethe in *Faust, I* (1790), and Shelley in *Queen Mab* (1812), *Alastor* (1816), and *Prometheus Unbound* (1819)—were to predict in their literature. Keats picks up evolution in *Hyperion* (1818-1819). In its changes from idyllic to horror visions of nature, evolution almost is the underpinning of "Epistle to J. H. Reynolds" (1818).

The idea is too large for illustrating by a segment of a poem. Rather, one must read all of, say, *Hyperion* to appreciate its evolution phase in Part II. Thereafter, one should attach the notion to character changes of the poet told to Moneta in the *Fall of Hyperion* (1819). And, if two examples are not enough, one should refer to the "Ode to a Nightingale" (1819) for the flicker-like changes of response by Keats to illness and songbird. True, the last two examples are ordinarily seen as psychological.

Idea 14. The immortality of nature, the mutability of man.

Late Victorians W. J. Courthope and Frances M. Owen recognize this idea in Keats's poetry, but without emphasis. An American poet, John Tabb, almost destroyed Keats's reputation with the claim that his immortality rests on the "scroll of nature."[30] The idea of the immortality of nature and the mutability of man had acceptance among German idealists of the eighteenth century and is prominent in *Werther* (1774) and in *Faust, Part I* (1790). The idea is related to nature's power to heal, to prophesy, and especially to renew itself. In the arrangement, nature is strong and durable. Man is weak and temporary. Witness the characterizations of Werther, Faust (in Part I), Childe Harold, Manfred, and Alastor. They illustrate without exception man's mutability before a seemingly immutable nature.

An artistic paraphrase of the immortality of nature and the mutability of man is Goethe's phrase in *Faust, I: Art ist lang, leben ist kurz,* Art is long, life is short. Keats's "Ode to a Nightingale" presents the immortality of nature in a bird while Keats, brother Tom, and biblical Ruth reveal the "fever and fret" of humankind. One has no proof that Keats knew that he had expressed the thesis in "Nightingale"; nor, for that matter, in "Written in Disgust of Vulgar Superstition" (1816), "On the Grasshopper and Cricket" (1816), or "Bright Star" (1819).

> The church bells toll a melancholy round,
>   Calling the people to some other prayers,
>   Some other gloominess, more dreadful cares,
> More hearkening to the sermon's horrid sound, ...
>   I should feel a damp . . .
>   did I not know . . .
>   ere they go
>   Into oblivion;—that fresh flowers will grow,
> And many glories of immortal stamp.
>   "Written in Disgust of Vulgar Superstition,"
>   ll. 1-4, 8-9, 12-14

> The poetry of earth is never dead: . . .
> The poetry of earth is ceasing never. . . .
>   "On the Grasshopper and Cricket," ll. 1, 9

> Bright star I would I were as steadfast as thou art—
>   "Bright Star!" l. 1

Idea 15. Nature's countryside preferred to man's city.

Except for Lamb and Blake, little choice existed for the literary Romantics on the matter. Nature, with its own life; with its capacity to stimulate, create nature-feelings, and be original, free, and novel in expression; nature with its capacity to reflect man's originality and disregard for rules; and nature with its celebration of man's emotion and offer of escape from the city—all made nature a countryside-haven for one wanting the best out of life.

Cowper, Beattie, Wordsworth, and Coleridge affirmed the countryside. Nature provided for them an idyllic respite, a "contented mind," gentle virtues, poetic imagination, and, not least, an emulation of Rousseau in his best censure of city worldliness and ambition.[31] The countryside they found is the pleasant scene, the Constable landscape of autumn, burnished haywains, happy children, and playful animals and brooks.

Another view of the countryside, yet preferable to the city, included the grandeur, starkness, and isolation of heights untouched by man and society. Byron in *Manfred* (1817) and *Childe Harold,* especially Canto III (1816), is the leading English proponent of the idea, but Mrs. Radcliffe and Wordsworth were aware of nature's height—and scope and awesomeness—in the *Mysteries of Udolpho* (1794) and in the *Prelude* (1805); also, Shelley in *Alastor* (1816) and *Prometheus Unbound* (1819), and Scott in *Guy Mannering* (1815) and *Rob Roy* (1818). The motif insured the impressiveness of nature and the triviality of man.

The Victorians did not celebrate either imprint of the countryside in Keats's poetry; nor, seemingly, did Keats beyond fulfillment of a convention. Still, one finds a peaceful countryside depicted in Keats's "O Solitude!" (1815). "To one who has been long in city pent" (1816), "Old Meg" (1818), "Mother of Hermes! and still youthful Maia" (1818), and "Character of Charles Brown" (1819).

> To one who has been long in city pent
>   'Tis very sweet to look into the fair
>   And open face of heaven, —to breathe a prayer
> Full in the smile of the blue firmament.
> Who is more happy, when, with heart's content,
>   Fatigued he sinks into some splendid lair
>   Of wavy grass, and read a debonair
> And gentle tale of love and languishment?
>   "To one who has been long in city pent," ll. 1-8

33

> Her brothers were the craggy hills
>> Her sisters larchen trees—
> Alone with her great family
>> She liv'd as she did please.

"Old Meg," ll. 9-12

> O Solitude! if I must with thee dwell,
> Let it not be among the jumbled heap
> Of murky buildings. . . .

"O Solitude!" ll. 1-3

Two more facts: first, the appeal of Nature's countryside, whether idyllic or awesome, coincides with Lovejoy's realistic observation of nature as (1) "antithetical to man and his works and untransformed by human art"; and, as (2) an out-of-doors of "natural sights and sounds" (Lovejoy 71). More than Beach or Neff, Lovejoy is in possession of this characteristic.

Second, the attention Keats gave to nature's countryside as a topic is not comparable to that he gave to nature's stimulation of the senses, Idea 8; to nature-feeling, Idea 3; to nature's literal landscapes, Idea 7; nor to nature's creation of a "thing of beauty," Idea 22, or nature's inspiring man to love, Idea 24.

The first three ideas on nature have Keats working at the stage of first sight and feeling, but with a response fresh and spontaneous. The last two ideas have Keats working after first sight and feeling to capture an in-depth relationship of man to nature and of nature to man. The first three ideas fall before the superior judgments on nature by Wordsworth in *Tintern Abbey,* Coleridge in "Frost at Midnight" and Shelley in "Mont Blanc." The last two ideas challenge the three poets in their best themes and images of nature.

Which would you have for a nature-display? Keats's collage of "Nightingale," "Melancholy," and *Hyperion,* or Coleridge's *Dejection: An Ode,* Shelley's "Ode to the West Wind," or Wordsworth's *Ode on Intimations of Immortality*?

Idea 16. Nature, a source of poetry.

Perhaps best stated by Wordsworth in the *Preface to the Lyrical Ballads* (1800) and well illustrated in three of his best poems, "The Solitary Reaper," "To the Cuckoo," and "I Wandered Lonely as a Cloud." Keats had a hand in the idea in "I stood tip-toe" (1816), *Sleep and Poetry* (1816), and *Endymion* (1817):

O Maker of sweet poets, dear delight
Of this fair world and all its gentle livers;
Spangler of clouds, halo of crystal rivers,
Mingler with leaves, and dew and tumbling streams. . .
Thee must I praise above all other glories. . . .
                              "I stood tip-toe," ll. 116-119, 123

        . . . [A] bowery nook
Will be elysium—an eternal book
Whence I may copy many a lovely saying
About the leaves, and flowers—about the playing
Of nymphs in woods, and fountains, and the shade
Keeping a silence round a sleeping maid;
And many a verse from so strange influence
That we must ever wonder how, and whence
It came.

                              Sleep and Poetry, ll. 63-71

Nature, a source of poetry: A dictum so accepted in Romantic aesthetics that to confute it even now is to be heretical. For Keats, then, to have accepted the theory in his time is a given. The remarkable part is that he did not express the theory more often, whatever his feeling for nature.

Nature, a source of poetry, is a simple commentary on the fact that nature stimulates man, Idea 8, and man communes with nature, Idea 2, and, from these interactions, a nature-feeling *(naturgefuhl)* is aroused, Idea 3. The nature-feeling becomes in its transference from nature to art a celebration of nature in the various arts. Thus, one has for a nature-setting Wordsworth's butterflies, John Marin's seascapes, and Charles Umlauf's garden-sculpture; for an idyllic nature, Beethoven's *Pastoral Symphony,* and Debussy's *La Mer,* and *Reflets dans l'eau;* and for an awesome nature, Debussy's *Cathedrale engloutie* and Chopin's "Winter Wind" etude.

Idea 17. Nature as a substitute for Christian orthodoxy (Neff, *Rev.* 167)

An early Shelleyan view in which Shelley attributed to nature what religious writers attributed to God. The idea can be found in Byron's *Childe Harold* (1812-1816) and *Manfred* (1817), but how seriously can be questioned. Often enough, Byron was merely concerned to shock.

The idea had real meaning for Wordsworth, one of whose missions in life was to instruct; and the idea, although not observed in Keats's poetry by either Romantic or Victorian critics, occurs in "Written in Disgust of Vulgar Superstition" (1816). A passage follows:

> The church bells toll a melancholy round,
>   Calling the people to some other prayers. . . .
> Still, still they toll, and I should feel a damp,
>   A chill as from a tomb, did I not know
>   . . . that fresh flowers will grow,
> And many glories of immortal stamp.
>
> ll. 1-2, 9-10, 13-14

The above passage reflects another thesis of Keats, that nature is immortal, man is mutable, Idea 14.

Idea 18. Nature as sacred (Beach 14; Neff, *Rev.* 171)

The judgment challenges but does not contradict nature seen as a substitute for Christian orthodoxy, Idea 17. As a kind of sacramental conclusion, the judgment was less and less popular among the Romantics after 1825. To be sure, it remained a viable topic, but without the thrust to dislodge a tendency of the nineteenth century to go along with the scientists in disengaging nature from God.

The tendency constitutes a contrast to the 18th-century attitudes of Schelling, Holderlin, and Novalis, who found "sacred" connotations in nature,[32] and to the 19th-century attitudes of Wordsworth, Coleridge, Emerson and Carlyle.[33] From their evidence, one can fashion this equation: the more visionary the Romantic, the more sacred his notion of nature. Thus one has Blake's mystical lamb and child in the *Songs of Innocence,*[34] and Emerson's premises on God and nature in the transcendental essays.[35]

Still, not Wesley, Keble, or Maurice, or Tennyson, Thomson, or Patmore could save nature for God from Lyell, the Darwins, Huxley, and Maxwell. Indeed, not even Gerard Manley Hopkins could, though he summoned up trout-moles, harvests, a kestrel, and even a typhoon as proofs of the workings of God in nature.[36]

One should not be surprised then that the idea does not concern Keats. I suggest that the idea be seen as a bas-relief revealing the temperament of a poet whose interest in nature is social and aesthetic rather than moral and, like Hopkins', religious.

Idea 19. Nature, preferable to human kind.

In its large sense, Nature, preferable to human kind, is a summing up, the apex of proofs that nature has been "naturing" well to man. In its small sense, Nature, preferable to human kind, is a corollary to one's preference of the countryside to the city, Idea 15. The felicities of nature are its space and quiet, its isolation and height, and its slowing of time, permitting one to be about essays, novels, poems, and philosophy embracing *naturgefuhl*.

A preference for nature by Byron is explicit in *Childe Harold,* (Cantos, I, II and III), and in *Manfred*. It is the underpinning of Wordsworth in the *Intimations of Immortality Ode*. Emery Neff observes that the preference is also evident in Victor Hugo's "Au Vallon de Cherizy" (1822; Neff, *Rev.* 170).

Perhaps surprisingly, the theme does not occur in Keats's poems, even though it should have, since it was related to an "influence" which he did accept: Nature as a human, instructive, and silent witness to others, Idea 25. Still, a letter to Reynolds, 19 February 1818, indicates Keats's awareness of theme.

> . . . I was led into these thoughts (on nature and man), my dear Reynolds, by the beauty of the morning operating on a sense of Idleness—I have not read any Books—the morning said I was right—I had no Idea but of the Morning and the Thrush said I was right. . . . (Rollins, ed. *Letters,* I, 232-233).

One finds the morning and the thrush—and quiet—in the countryside; one finds books and people—and clamor—in the city. The former sponsor an empathic and relaxing life; the latter, an intellective and stressful existence. Thus, for calm nerves, balanced head, and nature's *naturgefuhl,* nature has to be preferable to humankind.

D. Characteristics: *Natura Naturata*

Natura Naturata. Nature "natured." Generated and *natured* are better words for my purpose, for I would imply in the term the evidence that *natura* has achieved full bloom out of the bud-stage of *naturans*. Thus implied is the fact that nature has left its plateau of sensation and emotion to express that of thought and morality. *Natura naturata* is less objective and more social in meaning than *natura* in its *naturans* stage; indeed, it is nature operating in heights and depths above and below its physical and visual evidence.

One can envisage *natura naturans* as nature in a proliferation of concepts, of ever "becoming" since ever-groping for further being and value. On the other hand, *natura naturata* is set, "found," "become" in meaningfulness. It dwells where truths beyond facts and ideas beyond opinions have obtained, and change has become a lesser factor. It represents characteristics combined to bring about nature effects and influences. By comparison, it dwells at a center to which *natura naturans,* in its proliferation, is but epicenter.

Natura naturata also supplies underpinnings that *natura naturans* lacks. It offers hope that, deeper yet, a more clear and precise imprint of nature may emerge from what one has. The hope has its justification in Keats's Platonic glimpses of nature. The glimpses suggest that Nature, like the Great One of Plato, has its images of truth, goodness, and beauty, participating to be sure in Plato's triad, but arising out of its own characteristics *(naturans)* to become ultimate nature ideas *(naturata).*

1. Nature as Effect

Idea 20. Nature-feeling *(naturgefuhl)*

As an effect, nature-feeling is what one experiences from the unity of plants, animals, and man, Ideas 1-3; as a characteristic, it is the singular imprint whose vividness assures its recognition. I have mentioned that *joy* is the conspicuous effect of nature-feeling. I would add that fear and hate, and even horror, melancholy, and pity may also be emotions confirming the effect of nature upon the viewer. These emotions may be the prime evidences of the nature-feeling that we know.

Still, moods and states of being also have their occurrence from man's encounter with nature—moods like indolence, awe, and despair, and states like well-being, pleasure, and happiness. Moods and states of being represent the responses that nature "naturing" has stimulated. They go beyond sense but do not arrive at thought. They may reflect a moral motivation, but, in Keats's case, will more likely reflect an aesthetic. Either way, nature-feeling has become concrete—"felt"—and the term has become viable. I shall say that nature-feeling is most viable when seen as an effect. Indeed, as an effect, it has made cogent the need to have a metaphysics about nature.

Keats, a creature of emotions and moods, has dispensed emotions and moods in his nature poems. If "I stood tip-toe" and *Sleep and Poetry* project overflowing nature-feelings of the poet, the "Ode on Melancholy" and "Ode to a Nightingale" project moods in the reader so controlled as to produce authentic *naturgefuhl.* In "La Belle Dame" (1819), *Isabella* (1818), and *Lamia* (1819), the running mood, helped along by nature-motifs, is melancholy: the "blahs," if you please, in an all-but-felt presence. One's easy conclusion to them is that Keats wrote about what he felt, and that the nature elements in his poems reflect what mood or emotion invested him.

Poems reflecting well-being, pleasure, and happiness? Try "To Autumn" (1819) and *St. Agnes* (1819) for a pleasure replete in Keats; for well-being, try "Think not of it, sweet one, so . . ." (1817) and "On the Grasshopper and Cricket" (1816); for happiness, certainly "On Leigh Hunt's Poem," 'The Story of Rimini' " (1817) and "Robin Hood" (1818).

I shall not list segments of poems as illustrations of Keats's nature-effects. One must read the entire poem to get its effect, especially if, like "To Autumn" and "Robin Hood," the poem is short.

Idea 21. Nature as a "thing of beauty" (Beach 32).

Two family letters depict Keats's regard for a beautiful nature. To Tom Keats, 25-27 June 1818:

> . . .[T]he Lake and Mountain of Winander . . . surpass my expectation—beautiful water—shores and islands green to the marge—mountains all round up to the clouds . . . . [Our] two views [of the Lake] . . . are of the most noble tenderness . . .—they make one forget the divisions of life; . . . and refine one's sensual vision into a sort of north star which can never cease to be open-lidded and stedfast over the wonders of the great power (Rollins, ed. *Letters,* I, 298-299).

To Fanny Keats, 12 April 1819:

> There are some beautiful heaths now in bloom in pots . . . . I hope you have a good store of double violets—I

think they are the princesses of flowers and in a shower of rain, almost as fine as barley sugar drops are to a schoolboy's tongue (Rollins, ed. *Letters,* II, 51-52).

In the two letters, Keats's approach to nature's beauty is visual. The Victorian critics picked up this approach of Keats with a unanimity that almost atoned for their failure to see Keats's depiction of nature as ugly.

The idea of nature as beautiful is implicit in Lovejoy's full-blown equation of nature as that "containing necessary and self-evident truths concerning properties and the relation of essences" (Lovejoy, 72). The idea of nature as beautiful relates as well to Keats's belief in "the principle of beauty in all things," and in his *Endymion* line, "A thing of beauty is a joy forever."

If Keats found a rapport with nature's beauty, the Victorians found a rapport with Keats in treating the subject. The notion occurs not only in Keats's early, middle, and late poems—from "I stood tip-toe" (1816) to "Autumn" (1819) but also in the early, middle, and late Victorian criticisms of Keats. Of all the critics, only J.C. Shairp is negative on the subject. But not Palgrave who described the poet's nature-writing as "nature-painting," nor Gilfillan who found "ideal beauty" in the poet's nature lines. Then, W. T. Arnold was taken with Keats's way with England's landscape, and Matthew Arnold marveled at the "radiance" and "lightness" of Keats's nature descriptions.[37]

Still, the Victorian critics, however awakened to Keats's nature poems, never became as attached to them as to the Pre-Raphaelite, Grecian, and *l'art pour l'art* poems that made Keats their apostle of beauty. Nevertheless, the idea itself—nature as beautiful—helped to advance Keats in their eye from the infant to the maiden chamber of thought.[38] At first, the critics had been restrictive, confining Keats's view of nature to a roll-off of dreams, sensations, and emotions. By 1880, they had accepted his nature-work as showing a reality they could accept as thoughtful. *Hyperion,* "Ode on Melancholy," and "Ode to a Nightingale" were elemental in this critical conversion of the Victorians. In time, they came to salute one poem as the apogee of nature expression: "To Autumn." Robert Bridges declared "Autumn" to be the closest of Keats's odes to "perfection of workmanship."[39]

Nature as a "thing of beauty" gained Keats his reputation as a nature poet among the Victorian critics. The idea was major to them even as it was major to Keats. In the absence of address on the subject since 1935, the concept has lost its discussion. Thus, in the present, the Victorian opinion holds firm, the best to date of the nature-appreciations of Keats.

Two variants of nature as a "thing of beauty" are: Nature as good and beautiful, Idea 22, and Nature as beautiful and spacious; larger than the imagination can encompass, Idea 23. A justified conclusion from the variants is that the instances of nature as beautiful in Keats's poems are innumerable. Find them especially in "I stood tip-toe" (1816), *Sleep and Poetry* (1816), *Endymion* (1817), *Hyperion* (1818-1819), Ode to Melancholy" (1819), *Fall of Hyperion* (1819), and "To Autumn" (1819). Two other sources: "On Visiting the Tomb of Burns" (1818) and "Lines Written in the Highlands" (1818).

Instances:

> The clouds were pure and white as flocks new shorn,
> And fresh from the clear brook; sweetly they slept
> On the blue field of heaven, and then there crept
> A little noiseless noise among the leaves,
> Born of the very sigh that silence heaves:
> For not the faintest motion could be seen
> Of all the shades that slanted o'er the green.
>
> "I stood tip-toe," ll. 8-14

> What is more gentle than a wind in summer?
> What is more soothing than the pretty hummer
> That stays one moment in an open flower,
> And buzzes cheerily from bower to bower?
>
> *Sleep and Poetry*, ll. 1-4

> . . . yes, in spite of all,
> Some shape of beauty moves away the pall
> From our dark spirits. Such the sun, the moon,
> Trees old and young, sprouting a shady boon
> For simple sheep; and such are daffodils
> With the green world they live in; . . .
>
> *Endymion*, I, 11-16

> But when the melancholy fit shall fall
>   Sudden from heaven like a weeping cloud, . . .
> Then glut thy sorrow on a morning rose,

> Or on the rainbow of the salt sand-wave,
>   Or on the wealth of globed peonies; . . .
>   "Ode on Melancholy," 11. 11-12, 15-17

Idea 22. Nature as good and beautiful (Neff, *Rev.* 172-173).

The idea represents a middle link between a moral nature and an aesthetic one. The idea has a Greek patina, for it expresses two parts of the Greek triad—truth, goodness, and beauty—that Victoria's neo-Platonists saw better than the nature enthusiasts. Nature as good and beautiful, then, is certainly Platonic in source, and can be considered here as the miniature of the larger nature portrait in Idea 21, Nature as a "thing of beauty."

Keats included the good-and-beautiful theme in "The Poet" (1816), but the Victorians overlooked the theme in their eagerness to see the "pure" and the "Pre-Raphaelite" beauty that they sought. Neither poem nor idea has enjoyed a favorable landing since, probably because too close to nature as a "thing of beauty."

> At morn, at noon, at Eve, and Middle Night
>   He passes forth into the charmed air,
>   With talisman to call up spirits rare
> From plant, cave, rock, and fountain. —To his sight
> The hush of natural objects open quite
>   To the core; and every secret essence there
>   Reveals the elements of good and fair. . . .
>   "The Poet," 11. 1-7

(For Miriam Allott, this poem is questionably by Keats; Mabel Steele, Jack Stillinger, and probably John Taylor, Keats's publisher, felt the same. See Stillinger's *The Texts of Keats's Poems* [Cambridge: Harvard Univ. Press, 1974], p. 275, for an account.)

Idea 23. Nature as beautiful and spacious; larger than the imagination can encompass.

To Tom Keats, 25-27 June 1818:

> What astonishes me (about the waterfalls) more than
>   anything is the tone, the coloring, the slate, the stone,

> the moss, the rock-weed; or, if I may say so, the
> intellect, the countenance of such places. . . . The. . .
> magnitude of mountains and waterfalls are well imagined
> before one sees them; but this countenance or
> intellectual tone must surpass every imagination and
> defy any remembrance (Rollins, ed. *Letters,* I, 301).

Keats's opinion contradicts the Romantic thesis that the imagination embellishes nature in ways that nature cannot embellish the imagination. One can relax before Keats's humility and innocence when making an observation to Tom that has no subsequent expression in his poems. The idea has not been a theme for Victorian or 20th Century critic, and perhaps should not be. Its accuracy has been in doubt since the *Biographia Literaria* (1817).

Nature as beautiful and spacious and beyond the imagination's comprehension is, as said, a variant of Nature as "a thing of beauty," Idea 21. Near-antitheses of the notion occur in nature's having a cold beauty, Idea 34, and a sad beauty, Idea 35, a fact that reveals another near-antithesis: that nature is not independent of man, but can be what man would have nature to be—as, for instance, an effect of beauty or an influence on man.

2. Nature as Influence

The shift from nature's being a "thing of beauty" to nature's inspiring the "principle of love" represents a long step in what to do about nature. I judge that Keats, in his inexperience with a difficult subject, handled the shift less successfully than when he had captured nature as being a "thing of beauty." Beauty of course is not an easy subject to address, also; but love is more dimensional and subtle, and much more invasive and felt. With that difference in mind and considering the to-do Keats made of subject, one has to conclude that the poet recognized the principle's possibility. His inclusion of the idea may stop just short of becoming a flood.

Nature-as-good is the dominating impression in Keats's use of the "principle of love." Good rather than bad, gentle rather than rude. The notion has Keats brought into his most earnest nature stance, his participation as moralist. The role does not overwhelm Keats's participation as aesthete or intellectual; the role does substantiate what his letters, friendships, and poems reveal: that Keats had values and could judge. We are not better off for Keats's judgments as such, but nature is better off from the way he judged.

Idea 24. Nature inspires the "principle of love" (Beach 42).

The notion occurs throughout the Keats nature canon. One finds it in " 'O Solitude'!" (1816), "I stood tip-toe" (1816), *Sleep and Poetry* (1816), "Old Meg" (1818), "There is a joy in footing slow across a silent plain" (1818), and "Bards of passion and of mirth" (1818). Two other sources: "Ode to Psyche" (1819) and *Lamia* (1819).

In " 'O Solitude'!" the "principle," helped on by nature, appears as an expression of human fellowship. Here, nature serves not only as sponsor, but also as *naturegefuhl,* sealing a friendship.

> But though I'll gladly trace these scenes with thee,
> Yet the sweet converse of an innocent mind,
> Whose words are images of thoughts refin'd,
> Is my soul's pleasure; and it sure must be
> Almost the highest bliss of humankind,
> When to (nature's) haunts two kindred spirits flee.
>
> ll. 9-14

In *Sleep and Poetry,* because of nature, Keats turns

> . . . full hearted to the friendly aids,
> That smooth the path of honour; brotherhood,
> And friendliness, the nurse of mutual good.
>
> ll. 316-318

And Old Meg, fixed in nature, makes "mats of rushes,/And [gives] them to the cottagers/She met among the bushes" (ll. 21-24).

Wordsworth in *The Excursion* (1814) and Cowper in *The Task* (1785) provided Keats adequate precedents for seeing the "principle of love" inspired by nature; after Keats, Carlyle picked up the theme in *Sartor Resartus* (1833-4) as an instance of natural supernaturalism.

The Victorians missed the "principle of love" in Keats's poetry until 1876 when Frances Owen located the theme in *Endymion.* To be sure, the Victorians had noted the characteristic in Keats's poetry, but had related it to Keats's avidity for sensation, or to his sympathy for life.

Idea 25. Nature as an instructive, silent witness to others (Neff *Rev.* 168).

Nature, says Keats—and Beach, Lovejoy, and Neff discussing nature and Keats—is good, benevolent, moral: in all, a comforter of man. To Jane and Mariane Reynolds, 14 September 1817, Keats writes:

> . . . [I]n truth the great Elements we know of are no mean comforters—the open sky sits on our senses like a sapphire Crown—the Air is our Robe of State—the Earth is our throne and the sea a mighty Minstrell playing before it—able like David's harp to charm the evil spirit from such Creatures as I am—able like Ariel's to make sure a one as you forget almost the Tempest-cares of Life (Rollins, ed. *Letters,* I, 158).

Neff finds nature's helpfulness in Victor Hugo's *Aux Arbres* ("To Trees," 1856; *Rev.* 170). To his example, I would add that the Great Comforter shows up in "In drear-nighted December" (1817), "There is a joy in footing slow across a silent plain" (1818), and "On Fame" (1819). The three poems belong to Keats's entry into the second chamber of life where he is aware of both the pleasure and pain of life, and includes both in his poems. Not observed in these poems is a bit of Keatsian wit assayed as idea, that Nature is preferable in not being human.

> In drear-nighted December,
> Too happy, happy tree,
> Thy branches ne'er remember
> Their green felicity. . . .
>
> Ah! would 'twere so with many
> A gentle girl and boy—
> But were there ever any
> Writh'd not of passed joy?
> "On drear-nighted December," ll. 1-4, 17-20.
>
> How fever'd is the man, who cannot look
>   Upon his mortal days with temperate blood. . . .
> [See how] the Rose leaves herself upon the briar,

45

For winds to kiss and grateful bees to feed,
And the ripe plum still wears its dim attire,
   The undisturbed lake has crystal space,
   Why then should man, teasing the world for grace,
Spoil his salvation for a fierce miscreed?
                              "On Fame," ll. 1-2, 9-14

Idea 26. Nature as a source of health and spiritual insight (Neff, *Rev.,* 163-164).

This image of nature may be too much of a catch-all in yoking together two elements neither parallel nor opposed. Yet, Lovejoy makes note of similar functions of nature in its moral teaching and spiritual presence (Lovejoy 75); and Beach includes the Romantics' belief that nature is purposive, harmonious, and kind (Beach 6). Neff locates the nature notion in Keats's "What the Thrush Said" (1818, *Rev.* 164).

The Victorian critics found no instance in Keats's poetry of nature as a source of health and spiritual insight, but they were not looking for the idea, either. Actually, the idea shows up in *Sleep and Poetry* (1816), "On *The Story of Rimini*" (1817), "In drear-nighted December" (1817), and "Mother of Hermes! and still youthful Maia" (1818).

What is more tranquil than a musk-rose blowing
In a green island, far from all man's knowing?
More healthful than the leafiness of dales?
                              Sleep and Poetry, ll. 5-7

He who knows [nature's] delights, and, too, is prone
   To moralize upon a smile or tear,
Will find at once a region of his own,
   A bower for his spirit, and will steer
To alleys where the fir-tree drops its cone,
   Where robins hop, and fallen leaves are sere.
                              "On *The Story of Rimini,*" ll. 9-14

After dark vapours have oppressed our plains
   For a long dreary season, comes a day
   Born of the gentle south, and clears away
From the sick heavens all unseemly stains.
                              "After dark vapours," ll. 1-4

46

Idea 27. Nature as an influence on the poet.

Inevitably a topic compatible with Keats, and numerously illustrated in his poems. A confirmation of nature's influence appears in a letter to Benjamin Bailey, 18, 22 July 1818. The letter serves also to illustrate Nature as a stimulant of the senses, Idea 8.

> I should not have consented to myself these four
> months tramping in the highlands but that I thought it
> would give me more experience, . . . and strengthen
> more my reach in Poetry, than would stopping at
> home among Books, even though I should reach
> Homer—. . . . (Rollins, ed. *Letters,* I, 342)

In the poems, nature's influence on the poet appears in "How many bards" (1816), "I stood tip-toe" (1816), *Sleep and Poetry* (1816), and "Mother of Hermes! and still youthful Maia" (1818).

> . . . the unnumber'd sounds that evening store;
>   The songs of birds—the whisp'ring of the leaves—
>   The voice of waters—the great bell that heaves
> With solemn sound,—and thousands others more,
>   That distance of recognizance bereaves,
> Make pleasing music, and not wild uproar.
>   "How many bards," ll. 9-14

> O Maker of sweet poems, dear delight
> Of this fair world and all its gentle livers. . . .
>   "I stood tip-toe," ll. 116-117

>   . . . or, if I can bear
> The o'erwhelming sweets, 'twill bring me to the fair
> Visions of all places: a bowery nook
> Will be elysium—an eternal book
> Whence I may copy many a lovely saying
> About the leaves, and flowers—about the playing
> Of nymphs in woods, and fountains, and the shade
> Keeping a silence round a sleeping maid. . . .
>   *Sleep and Poetry,* ll. 61-68

> Mother of Hermes! and still youthful Maia!
>   May I sing to thee
> As thou wast hymned on the shores of Baiae?
>   Or may I woo thee

In earlier Sicilian? or thy smiles
Seek as they once were sought in Grecian isles
By bards who died content on pleasant sward,
Leaving great verse unto a little clan?

"Mother of Hermes!" ll. 1-8

The idea is not comparable in magnitude to the larger influence, Nature itself, an example for art, Idea 29. It remains nevertheless a cogent reminder that nature to Keats—and to the Romantics—possessed poetic motivations that we have denied for ourselves.

A variant of Nature as an influence on the poet is Nature, a source of poetry, Idea 30. *Naturlich!* Nature is a source of poetry if nature is also an influence on the poet. The facts in their repetition reflect more linguistic whim than factual difference.

Idea 28. Nature, a rebuke to man's inhumanity to man.

The idea is necessary. It requires but a summation of nature's service to the good person to conclude that nature would also rebuke the bad one. The service projects the image of a hovering Mother, larger than man, ready like the Greek gods to intervene, define, and correct. The idea is relatively unimportant in the Keats nature canon. Still, the idea is pertinent in "Ode to a Nightingale" (1819). I should add that an even more challenging representation is to be found in Shelley's "Mont Blanc" (1816). A passage in "Nightingale" follows:

Fade far away, dissolve, and quite forget
  What thou among the leaves hast never known,
The weariness, the fever, and the fret
  Here, where men sit and hear each other groan;
Where palsy shakes a few, sad, last-gray hairs,
  Where youth grows pale, and specter-thin, and
  dies. . . .

ll. 21-26

Idea 29. Nature, itself, an example for art.

The theory assumes the existence of an ideal or an emulable nature providing justification for the aesthetic that art should imitate nature. Lovejoy's interpretation of the idea is suggestive: Nature, he says, becomes a "personified, or half-personified, power illustrating attributes or modes of working that should characterize human art"

(Lovejoy 72).

Nature as an example of art has at least two ways of expression in Keats's poetry: through literal statement of the subject—less likely in Keats's case—and, to repeat, through raising nature to a "personified" or "half-personified" state. "Personified" finds nature become symbolic, archetypal, or Greek personified. "Half-personified" finds nature short of these developed states. To mark the difference, I would define the sun-image in *Sleep and Poetry* (ll. 125-162) as "half-personified"; that is, the sun is living, but is not archetypal or Greek in identification.

I do not underestimate the subtlety required in sizing up many a full or half-personification of nature. The situation calls for a skillful reader and a communicable poem. If, for instance, one spends time on a poem's meaning, he can have lost the nature-personification. If one has read a poem too casually or closely, he runs a risk of not recognizing the image. I am saying, then, that nature-personifications of the kind I am speaking ought to exist, but we have the habit of not letting them except as a Grecian device. Thus, lost is an important identification of nature as an example of art.

Three more on the nature personification short of its Greek expression: one, the half is more subtle than the whole and requires closer analysis; two, Keats, without mentioning the half, seems to have doted on it; three, Keats's description of poetry having to come as easily as leaves on a tree exactly half-personifies the effect of inspiration in the poet.

Lovejoy says that the role of nature characterizing "human art" is shown in its fullness, abundance, and variety of content (Lovejoy 72). Both the Romantics and the Victorians praised these attributes in Shakespeare, but carped about Keats's excess of them in *Endymion*. Generally, the notions of nature characterizing "human art" proved to be either too subtle or too vague for the critics' acceptance, or else the critics lacked time and precedent to put Keats's poems under a microscope.

Keats's notion of nature characterizing human art is, of course, viable. One needs only to accept his personifications to recognize their art. One has the full personification, achieved best in the long poem, and humanized as a vivid and relevant element; and the half-personification found more often in the short poem, and humanized as a vivid but less dimensional element. The examples to follow will not exhaust those present in Keats's "On the Grasshopper and

49

Cricket'' (1816), *Sleep and Poetry* (1816), "When I have fears that I may cease to be" (1818), "To Fanny" (1819), "Not Aladdin Magian" (1818), "To Ailsa Rock," (1818), and "Ode to Psyche'' (1819).

Note the "Ode to Psyche": nature has become a personified power and an artistic example.

> O Goddess! hear these tuneless numbers, wrung
>   By sweet enforcement and remembrance dear,
> And pardon that thy secrets should be sung
>   Even into thine own soft-conched ear:
> Surely I dreamt today, or did I see
>   The winged Psyche with awaken'd eyes?
>
> "Ode to Psyche," ll. 1-6

In "Read me a lesson, Muse, and speak it loud," nature has become the instance for (a work of) art:

> Read me a lesson, Muse, and speak it loud
>   Upon the top of Nevis, blind in mist!
> I look into the chasms, and a shroud
>   Vaprous doth hide them; just so much I wist
> Man-kind do know of hell: I look o'erhead,
>   And there is sudden mist, even so much
> Mankind can tell of heaven: mist is spread
>   Before the earth, beneath me; even such,
> Even so vague is man's sight of himself.
>
> ll. 1-9

Then, nature, half-personified:

> A theme! a theme! Great Nature! give a theme;
>   Let me begin my dream.
> I come—I see thee, as thou standest there,
> Beckon me out into the wintry air.
>
> "To Fanny," ll. 5-8

And, again, nature as example for (a work of) art:

> When I behold upon the night's starr'd face,
>   Huge cloudy symbols of a high romance,
> And think that I may never live to trace
>   Their shadows, with the magic hand of chance;. . .
>
> "When I have fears," ll. 5-8

Idea 30. Nature revealed in man's feeling at the expense of his intellect; in his freedom from reflective design; and in his joy in nature (Lovejoy 74).

Already cited as a characteristic of *natura naturans,* the idea, in all its clutter of facts, represents also an influence of nature on man. Implicit in the relationship of nature to man is the fact that nature, greater in power, supplies nature-feelings that man cannot, encourages man's feeling at the expense of his reasoning, and possesses a freedom beyond that of man. Man's trap is to be rational; his deliverance is to be natural. That he is natural is reflected in the doings of nature in his actions.

An example of nature's fine tunings in man are in Idea 12, of the same description as the above. Only a reshaping of one's nature view from *characteristic* to *influence* is needed to find the examples in Idea 12 appropriate to this "influence" idea.

Idea 31. Nature, a stimulant of the senses.

The idea is better interpreted as a characteristic of nature than as an influence. Still, nature is influential when it becomes a stimulant of man's senses. Not irrelevant is the fact that nature's influence on man at this level is in its rawest state, causing sensations and perhaps emotions and moods, but not impressions, ideas, or teachings.

I refer the reader to Nature as stimulant, Idea 8, for apt examples in Keats's letters and his poems. I would thereafter have the reader forget the status of nature, stimulant, as an influence. It serves too little purpose to warrant development.

II. Nature's Negatives

Neither Victorians nor moderns have stressed nature's flaws as much as her virtues; still, nature's role today has been determined by their awareness of her flaws. By the 1840's, the English Victorian and, as Vigny shows, the French Romantic were on to something wrong in the nature set-up. The 20th-century modern has done nothing to allay that suspicion. In the long blight pursuing nature since 1807, the biologists and botanists have reduced her to a classification of parts; the poets have abandoned her except as background or after-thought;

and the entrepreneurs have exploited her natural wealth.

Before the 1950's, nature's animals, forests, fish, plants, waters, and reptiles had gone under to re-appear as civilization's furs, lumber, protein, fiber, sewage, and belts and boots. Since the 1950's, the ways of saving nature have obtained to the extent that one can envisage that there will remain a nature. Still, nature's salvation today is of man's doing, not of nature's. Such a situation, at best, only signifies a reversal of the Romantics' dependence on nature; at worst, it is man's epitaph sealing nature's doom even more than when Keats foresaw the broken chain of being among animals, plants, and man.

As nature's flaws in this study should suggest, Keats had a realistic eye for nature. To be sure, he also saw more good in nature than bad, and this fact may reveal that Keats, during his poetry years, 1815-1820, was yet too close to Wordsworth's nature sonnets and odes, 1802-1805, for more direful assessments of nature on his part. Viewed *in toto,* Keats's nature poems—and his nature facts in other poems—do pick up much of the after-glow of nature's diminishing light. Thus, what one finds in Keats on nature is a fractured insight, one full of oppositions and catch-alls, yet demonstrating a coherence of development that Shelley and Byron did not achieve in their decades with nature.

A great merit of Keats's regard for nature is that, as much as his decade permitted, he saw her in a doubled light, as Mother and Witch, flawless and flawed, and dominating and supine. At the same time, he allowed neither trumpery nor hi-jinks, and neither reverence nor enmity, to interrupt his vision. He saw her, rather, as an ironic expression of pluses and minuses, and with that conclusion he took his stand. Perhaps that is enough of a credential for one Romantic yet as fresh and wet before life in 1821 as that ironic speck showing up in his sputum.

A. Nature Metaphysics

Idea 32. The broken chain of being among plants, animals, and man.

The contradiction, at last, of Herder's cosmical unity among plants, animals, and man, Idea 1.

Keats was not being intentionally profound when he expressed the idea in ''I had a dove and the sweet dove died'' (c. 1818); still, he had picked up a notion of nature already accepted by other Romantics. Wordsworth's "Ode to Duty," 1805, presumes the broken chain of being in Wordsworth's abdication of nature's law for society's order; his "Elegiac Stanzas" (1805) and River Duddon sonnets (1820) confirm that broken state in the evidence of nature's turbulence and civilization's conquest. The notion may relate to an apprehension of the poets of the Age over the inroads of science on not only nature, but also the literary imagination. I incline to believe that Keats had the broken chain in mind in his attack on knowledge in *Lamia* (1819).

The broken chain of being among plants, animals, and man was recognized by Victorians Tennyson, Swinburne, and Arnold, and by modernist Hardy;[40] it received less recognition by critics like Masson, Colvin and Bridges. The latter, in fact, found no evidence of the idea in Keats's poetry. But there it was. See the examples below.

I had a dove, and the sweet dove died,
  And I have thought it died of grieving;
O what could it grieve for? Its feet were tied
  With a silken thread of my own hand's weaving;
Sweet little red feet! Why should you die? . . .
You liv'd alone in the forest-tree,
Why, pretty thing, could you not live with me?
                    "I had a dove," ll. 1-5, 7-8

        Do not all charms fly
At the mere touch of cold philosophy?
There was an awful rainbow once in heaven:
We know her woof, her texture; she is given
In the dull catalogue of common things.
Philosophy will clip an Angel's wings,
Conquer all mysteries by rule and line,
Empty the haunted air, and gnomed mine—
Unweave a rainbow, as it erstwhile made
The tender-person'd Lamia melt into a shade.
                    Lamia, II, 229-238

It is pertinent to see the next flaws of nature noted by Keats as results of nature's broken chain of being. Surely, one has to see that, in her broken state, nature has lost the magnitude and scope, and the effect and influence, displayed from Rousseau to Wordsworth; and, worse, has in modern state become man's pawn. How obviously we accept the fact that man can praise or dispraise nature as finished or

53

unfinished, but nature cannot do the same with man. I am saying, then, that Keats's disparagements of nature to follow are as illuminating as unfortunate and as realistic to include as necessary to admit.

B. Characteristics. *Natura Naturans*

Idea 33. Humanity as preferable to nature.

Said Keats to Bailey, 13 March 1818: Scenery is fine—but human nature is finer . . ." (Rollins, ed. *Letters,* I, 242). The comment enforces a sentiment expressed in "To My Brother George" in 1816:

> But what without the social thought of thee,
> Would be the wonders of the sky and sea?
>
> ll. 13-14

Keats's statement precedes Alfred de Vigny's assault on nature in *La Maison des Bergers* ("The Shepherd's Hut," 1844); they follow Wordsworth's social and religious poetry after 1815.

The idea of humanity as preferable to nature contradicts the idea that nature is preferable to human-kind, Idea 19. It is perhaps the most predictable contradiction of nature by not only Keats but also Wordsworth, Coleridge, Goethe, and Shelley.[41]

Idea 34. Nature as having a cold beauty.

The idea rebuts the warming, positive concept of Nature as a "thing of beauty," Idea 21. It dissipates the notion that between nature and man there exists *naturgefuhl,* Idea 3. The idea thus becomes an emphatic illustration of a state no longer good among plants, animals and man.

> The town, the churchyard, and the setting sun,
>   The clouds, the trees, the rounded hills all seem,
>   Though beautiful, cold—strange—as in a dream. . .
> All is cold beauty. . . .
>   "On Visiting the Tomb of Burns" (1818), ll. 1-3, 8

Idea 35. Nature as having a sad beauty.

The idea is projective in "There is a joy in footing slow across a silent plain" (1818) and in "Ode to Melancholy" (1819). The concept challenges the notion in Idea 26 of Nature as a source of health and insight, and in Idea 5, Nature as *la belle nature*.

Neither the nineteenth- nor the twentieth-century critics have given time to this Keatsian idea, despite its arresting paradox that nature's beauty can be sad.

> There is a deeper joy than all, more solemn in the
>   heart,
> More parching to the tongue than all, of more divine
>   a smart,
> When weary feet forget themselves upon a pleasant
>   turf,
> Upon hot sand, or flinty road or sea-shore iron scurf
>   Toward the castle or the cot where long ago was
>   born
> One who was great through mortal days and died of
>   fame unshorn!
> Light heather-bells may tremble then . . .;
> Wood-lark may sing from sandy fern, — . . .;
> Runnels may kiss the grass on shelves and shallows
>   clear,
> But their low voices are not heard, though come on
>   travels drear. . . .
> > > "There is a joy in footing slow across a silent
> > > > plain" (1818), ll. 7-16

Idea 36. Nature, a dangerous delight, withdrawing one from human sympathy (Neff, *Rev.* 169)

Keats expresses the view in "I stood tip-toe" (1816), and ambiguously, as we shall see, in *Lamia* (1819). Shelley expresses better the same view in *Alastor* (1816).

In each instance, at stake is the positive, burgeoning sentiment of nature as preferable to humankind, Idea 19. In 1816, however, to many Romantics, nature could be too easily a suspect, if not a dangerous, delight.

> Was there a Poet born?—but now no more,
> My wand'ring spirit must no further soar.—
> > > "I stood tip-toe," ll. 241-242

In *Lamia*, nature becomes a dangerous delight in Lamia's

attraction of Lycius away from Apollonius and knowledge. To include a segment of *Lamia* as illustration of this fact is to miss the greater "menace" of nature illustrated by the whole poem.

Idea 37. Nature is less than human nature.

The notion sums up Keats's dislocation from nature. The notion belongs in Keats's "maiden chamber" of thought, and would have rested easily in a third or fourth chamber, had Keats the liberty and time to keep adding to his big house. The observation is simple, conclusive, and, above all, mature. But, here, it is preliminary to what might have been had Keats withdrawn from his nature poetry to complete the *Fall of Hyperion* (1819) and whatever else was to have followed the *Fall*.

Nature's being less than human nature does not show up in literal statement in Keats's poems, but Keats's remark on the fact is to the right person, the aspirant-in-theology Benjamin Bailey, 13 March 1818. Therefore, repeated:

> Scenery is fine—but human nature is finer . . .
> (Rollins, ed. *Letters,* I, 242).

One can assume that Keats would have wanted the expression to occur in a poem, its value having achieved concretion in his mind.

C. Characteristics. *Natura Naturata*

1. Effect

Idea 38. Nature as ugly, horrible, and vicious.

The notion marks the reversal of nature seen as idyllic, beautiful, benevolent, and healthful, Ideas 5, 21, 25, and 26, respectively.

A Gothic insight, the notions reach into nature's hell, the storms, earthquakes, droughts, fires, avalanches, and floods apparent to any naturalist. More alarming, the insight, as with Wordsworth, Coleridge, Shelley, and Keats, draws upon the morbid depths in us all.

Overall, the concept questions man's communing with nature, and nature's with man, Idea 2; it renders abject man's natural feelings for nature, Idea 3. The concept damages the optimism of man that nature is a part of a cosmical unity that includes man, Idea 1; and, worst of all, it renders nature as a malevolent force. If previously one saw frolicsome lambs on the hillside with a shepherd at hand, one now sees the sinister wolf in the shepherd's absence. The concept compels response, invites trauma, and creates confusion. The concept did these things to both Shelley and Wordsworth, but less so to Keats. Indeed, after 1817, Keats did not lose his balance about nature, whatever the beatitude or crisis.

Strangely, this fact: the Victorians overlooked the Keatsian notion of nature as ugly, horrible, and vicious. Yet, they had a background of writings by Goethe, Malthus, and Erasmus Darwin from 1782 to 1807, and by Charles Darwin, Herbert Spencer, George Moore, and Thomas Hardy from 1835 to 1895, to advise them on the concept.

They also had Keats. Keats recognized such a state of nature in *Sleep and Poetry* (1816), *Isabella* (1818), "Epistle to J.H. Reynolds" (1818), and "To Ailsa Rock" (1818). To these poems must be added an awakened sentiment on nature as dangerous in "Ode on Melancholy" (1819) and "To Fanny" (1819).

Ernest De Selincourt detected in 1905 the savagery of nature in the "Epistle to J. H. Reynolds." De Selincourt undoubtedly aroused the awareness of other 20th-century scholars on the subject. I cite particularly Hoxie Neale Fairchild's exploration of the subject in "Keats and the Struggle-for-Existence Tradition" (*PMLA*, LXIV, 1949).

The topic is a favorite of Keats's, a fact that may illumine Keats's attraction to the perverse as well as his willingness to accept that nature is both good and bad. Wrote Keats to Bailey, 13 March 1818: "[T]he abominable Devonshire Weather . . . is . . . splashy, rainy, misty, snowy, foggy, haily, floody, muddy, slipshod. . . . The hills are very beautiful when you get a sight of 'em." (Rollins, ed. *Letters*, I, 241).

In the same year, more seriously:

> Dear Reynolds! . . .
>   . . . I was at home,
> And should have been most happy—but I saw
> Too far into the sea; where every maw
> The greater on the less feeds evermore: — . . .
> Still do I that most fierce destruction see. —
> The shark at savage prey—the hawk at pounce,
> The gentle robin, like a pard or ounce,
> Ravening a worm. — . . . .
>   "Epistle to J. H. Reynolds," ll. 86, 92-95, 102-105

And in 1818:

> For (the two brothers) the Ceylon diver held his
>   breath,
>   And went all naked to the hungry shark;
> For them his ears gush'd blood; for them in death
>   The seal on the cold ice with piteous bark
> Lay full of darts. . . .
>
> *Isabella; or the Pot of Basil,* ll. 113-117

In 1819, in "What can I do to drive away":

> Where shall I learn to get my peace again?
> To banish thoughts of that most hateful land,
> Dungeoner of my friends, that wicked strand
> Where they were wreck'd and live a wrecked life;
> That monstrous region, whose dull rivers pour
> Ever from their sordid urns unto the shore,
> Unown'd of any weedy-haired gods; . . .
> There flowers have no scent, birds no sweet song,
> And great unerring Nature once seems wrong.
>
> ll. 30-36, 42-43

Then, in "Ode on Melancholy" (1819):

> No, no, go not to Lethe, neither twist
>   Wolf's bane, tight-rooted, for its poisonous wine. . .
> Make not your rosary of yew-berries,
>   Nor let the beetle, nor the death-moth be
>   Your mournful Psyche, nor the downy owl
> A partner in your sorrow's mysteries. . . .
>
> ll. 1-2, 5-8

Nature as ugly, horrible, and vicious is a fitting conclusion to "Keats and Nature" in representing a large statement on a major outcropping of nature. It reveals Keats firmly planted on the terrain about him. It reveals Keats as knowledgeable about the dangers of life even as he contemplates its beauties. In all, it is the needed clincher to the fact that Keats could see nature as more than idyll, dream, or revel. For this fact, and for many others, we owe a gratitude to Keats on nature that we cannot give as easily to Wordsworth before 1807, to Coleridge after 1802, or to Byron after 1817.

2. Influence

No ideas of nature as bad exist as more than a momentary influence in the Keats collocation on nature. That nature, bad, can constitute a major influence we know in the case of Wordsworth and Coleridge.[42] With Keats, the influence may be tentative enough not to be serious. As we know of Keats, nature has a sad beauty or a cold beauty, or can be a dangerous delight. These are losses, not catastrophes. They tell one, for instance, that nature was being superseded, neutralized, and condemned—piece-mealed, then, by those zealots of the Age: the utilitarian, the scientist, the entrepreneur, and, yes, the Victorian poet.

Keats's sympathy for mankind, made clear in the concluding characteristics, would have been at stake had he sponsored the malignity of nature as an influence. Even Hardy, divorced from the benevolence of nature, could not say more than that the collision of an iceberg with the Titanic was determined, not influenced. The fact is that a harmful nature become credo can get one into the baleful world of idols, magic, and hallucinations.

This step was not to be Keats's. Rather, nature as ugly, horrible, and vicious seems to have constituted for him an imbalance reminding one that nothing is perfect, not even nature; indeed, reminding one that for every beauty of nature, there can be an ugliness and, for every evidence of nature's love, there can exist the evidence of her viciousness. Still, this difference is also a part of the testimony: the love and beauty in nature of which he writes show better and more often than her horror or ugliness. Thus, Keats on nature. I find him an example that one can accept.

Endnotes

[1] For one reference on Herder, see Emery Neff's *The Poetry*

of History. New York: Columbia Univ. Press (1947), pp. 71-72. Other meritorious references on Herder include Frederick M. Barnard, *Herder's Social and Political Thought.* Oxford: Clarendon Press (1967); Hugh Barr Nisbet, *Herder and the Philosophy and History of Science.* Cambridge: MHRA (1970); and especially Robert Thomas Clark, *Herder: His Life and Thought.* Berkeley: Univ. of California Press (1955).

[2] *The Letters of John Keats 1814-1821.* Edited by Hyder Edward Rollins. Cambridge: Harvard Univ. Press (1958), II, 79. Hereafter cited in the text as *Rollins, ed. Letters.*

[3] See Idea 32 for comment on the broken chain of being among plants, animals, and man.

[4] See "Shakespeare (His Characteristics)" in *Coleridge: Select Poetry and Prose.* Edited by Stephen Potter. London: Nonesuch Press (1933), p.339.

[5] A thesis of Shelley is that poetry is mimetic—a reproduction of life occurring in society and nature. The poet, looking to nature, and to society, achieves through use of the imagination the highest and most pleasurable expression of what he reproduces. See Shelley's *A Defense of Poetry.* Edited by John E. Jordan. Indianapolis: Bobbs-Merrill (1965), pp. 28-30. A Library of Liberal Arts Edition.

[6] Another letter on man's communion with nature, this one to J.H. Reynolds, 21 September 1819: "How beautiful the season is now—How fine the air. A temperate sharpness about it. Really, without joking, chaste weather—Dian skies—I've never liked stubble fields so much as now—Aye better than the chilly green of the spring. Somehow a stubble plain looks warm—in the same way that some pictures look warm . . ." (Rollins, ed. *Letters,* II, 167).

[7] Two major Keatsians on Keats' (and man's) communion with nature: John Middleton Murry in "The Realms of Gold," *Keats.* London: Jonathan Cape (1955), pp. 145-165, and Sidney Colvin in *John Keats.* London: Macmillan (1917), pp. 21-22, 79-80, 122-123, and 215-219. Hereafter, the 1917 biography by Colvin to be cited in the text as *Colvin 1917.*

[8] See "Notes," *Poems of John Keats.* Ed. Ernest De Selincourt. London: Methuen (1951 ed.), p. 389. Hereafter cited in the text as *De Selincourt.*

[9] For facts about the breakdown between nature and Leopardi, Tennyson, Leconte de Lisle, Baudelaire, and Arnold, see Emery Neff's "Nature," *A Revolution in European Poetry.* New York:

Columbia Univ. Press (1940), pp. 157-190. To Neff's listing there, add Thomas Hardy's late-century poems on nature's enigmatic and terrifying way.

[10] *Naturgefuhl* (Ger.) is better usage than its translation "nature-feeling" to connote the felt relationship of man with nature. For variety of communication, I shall use both terms in this study. A.O. Lovejoy uses *naturgefuhl* in "Nature as an Aesthetic Norm," *Essays in the History of Ideas.* Baltimore (1941), p. 75. References to Lovejoy's "Nature as an Aesthetic Norm" hereafter cited in the text as *Lovejoy.*

[11] One more example, the most felt of the instances of *naturgefuhl:*

> Open afresh your round of starry folds,
> Ye ardent marigolds!
> Dry up the moisture from your golden lids,
> for great Apollo bids
> That in these days your praises should be sung
> On many harps, which he has lately strung. . . .
>
> *I stood tip-toe*, ll. 47-52.

[12] My paraphrase of Schelling's concept of nature as visible spirit and spirit as invisible nature. Mentioned in Neff's *A Revolution in European Poetry,* p. 161. Hereafter *Neff's Revolution,* cited in the text as *Neff, Rev.*

[13] See Joseph Warren Beach, *The Concept of Nature in Nineteenth-Century English Poetry.* New York: Macmillan (1936), and Neff, *A Revolution in European Poetry* (1940) for expanded treatments of nature as visible thought, thought as invisible nature. Especially valuable in Beach's study are "Introduction and Conclusion," pp. 3-27; "Wordsworth's Naturalism," pp. 110-157, and "Wordsworth and Nature's Teachings," pp. 158-201; "Carlyle," pp. 301-317; and "Coleridge, Emerson, and Naturalism," pp. 318-345. In Neff's study, "Nature," pp. 157-190. References to Beach's *The Concept of Nature...* hereafter cited in the text as *Beach.*

[14] London (1876), pp. 84-85.

[15] See Noel, *Essays on Poetry and Poets.* London (1886), pp. 159-160.

[16] *La belle nature.* [Un] ideal valorisant l'art antique elaboree dans la l[re] moitie du 17[e] s. . . . et devenu un concept-cle de la critique esthetique en France aux 17[e] et 18[e] siecles. *[Tr[e]sor de la Langue Francaise Dictionnaire* du XIX[e] et du XX[e] Siecle. Paris: Gallimard, 1986. XII, 16.]

61

The term has never gained real currency in English aesthetics, especially its literary aesthetics. The term is relevant here for revealing a perennial tendency of the West since the Renaissance to measure its art by classical values.

[17] One's truest way into the Platonic profundities of Nature is by application of its meanings to the arguments in Plato's *Symposium, Phaedrus* and *Phaedo. Nature* is not the theme of these dialogues, but the arguments there of why to shun matter, sensation and imagination to effect enduring concepts of the spirit will apply to Nature. I refer you to *The Dialogues of Plato.* Trans. by Benjamin Jowett. New York: Random House (1937), I, 233-282; 301-345; 441-501.

[18] One has only to get into the *OED* to witness a flow of meanings of *Nature,* including its Latin forebear *natura* (Oxford: Clarendon Press, 1933-1961; VII, N-POY, 41-42). I do not regard as amiss therefore my putting together yet another meaning, this time in connection with uses of *natura* as *naturans* (pres. part.) and *naturata* (past part.). I should warn, however, that my uses not only differ from Spinoza's but contradict the Middle Ages', including those of St. Thomas Aquinas. To Aquinas, *natura naturans* indicates God's creativity at work; *natura naturata,* the result, the universe. My uses project *natura naturans* as fledgling particulars, on the lowest instead of the highest rung of the nature ladder. They project *natura naturata* on the highest rung, the principle emerged from the particulars in a significant effect or influence.

Let me illustrate. Nature as a "thing of beauty"—an instance of *natura naturata*—includes (1) a stimulation of the senses of the viewer; (2) the viewer's feelingful response; (3) a recognition of not only nature's symmetry and form, and freedom and novelty, but also (4) its potentiality as an expression of art. Seen, individually, the four characteristics are participants in *natura naturans;* collectively, they become a culminating imprint, a "thing of beauty," *naturata.*

See the *Lexicon Latinitatis Medii Aevi Dictionnaire Latin-Francais des Auteurs du Moyen-Age* (Ed. Albert Blaise. Turnholti, 1975, p. 612) for accepted medieval interpretations of *natura naturans* and *naturata,* then read Spinoza's interpretations and, finally, mine again before awarding either exculpation or damnation to the third participant in this gala display of nature meanings.

[19] Ruskin's complaint against the Romantics for humanizing nature helped him into related stands against Keats, despite his high ratings of Keats in *Modern Painters* and *Pre-Raphaelitism.* For

instance, to Ruskin, Keats's joy over nature was a poetic distraction; Keats's love of nature illustrated a poet of imagination, sympathy, and somewhat religious principles overthrown by his passions. Then, Keats's nature descriptions signalled to Ruskin a poet unable to write about human problems. Not least, Keats's love of nature's beauty impressed him as unsympathetic and violent. Ruskin's comments, in *Modern Painters* (London, 1906, III, 256, 258, 272-273), belong to the rising Victorian tide of anti-nature and anti-Romantic commentary.

[20] For Arnold's description of nature, see "To An Independent Preacher Who Preached That We Should Be in 'Harmony with Nature' " (c. 1849). Arnold concludes: "Nature and man can never be fast friends./Fool, if thou canst not pass her, rest her slave"!

[21] The Pre-Raphaelites had made strong allowance for nature's beauty in the Pre-Raphaelite Manifesto. Yet, as the century went into its second half, an obvious trend of the Pre-Raphaelites was toward medieval legend, literary themes, and a mystique suffused with heaven, fair maidens, and Camelot. All espoused nobly and gently, to be sure, but hardly with joy of nature as a robust complement.

[22] For representative Victorian opinions of Keats's literal descriptions of nature, see George Gilfillan, *A Gallery of Literary Portraits*. London (1845), p. 380; J. C. Shairp, *On Poetic Interpretation of Nature*. Boston (1877), p. 43; Edmund Scherer, "Wordsworth and Modern Poetry in England," *Essays on English Literature*. Trans. by George Saintsbury. New York (1891); Sidney Colvin, *John Keats*. London (1917); Francis Turner Palgrave, *Landscape in Recent Poetry*. London (1897); Arthur C. Downer, *The Odes of Keats*. Oxford (1897), p. 10. Hereafter Scherer to be cited in the text as *Scherer;* Downer, as *Downer;* Colvin as in f.n. 7, *Colvin 1917.*

[23] Robert Bridges, *John Keats, a Critical Essay*. Privately printed. London (1895). Hereafter to be cited in the text as *Bridges*.

[24] "Wise passiveness." Wordsworth is in the state in "Expostulation and Reply," and *Tintern Abbey*. He is not, in the *Ode on Intimations of Immortality*, the "Ode to Duty," and the "Elegiac Stanzas" (in memory of his brother John Wordsworth).

[25] See A.C. Swinburne, *Complete Works,* XV, 109. Eds. [Sir] Edmund Gosse and T.J. Wise. London (1925-1927); David Masson, *Wordsworth, Shelley, and Keats*. London (1875), p. 66. Scherer, "Wordsworth and Modern Poetry in England," p. 192; Colvin, *Keats*. New York (1887), Richard Henry Stoddard, "Introduction,"

Selections from the Poetical Works of A.C. Swinburne. New York (1884), p. 43; and Robert Bridges, *John Keats, A Critical Study,* pp. 88, 90. Hereafter, references to Masson, Colvin, and Stoddard to be cited in the text as *Masson, Colvin 1887,* and *Stoddard.*

[26] Stoddard is American; Scherer, French. Both are "Victorian" in their concept of poetry and approaches to Keats.

[27] *Kant on genius.* See Kant's *Critique of Judgment.* Great Books of the Western World. Trans. James Creed. Chicago (1955), XLII, 525-526. Hereafter cited in the text as *Kant.*

[28] David Masson exclaimed over Keats's joy in nature in *Wordsworth, Shelley, and Keats,* p. 186; Courthope commented adversely on Keats's freedom from reflective design in "Keats's Place in Poetry," *The National Review,* X (Sept., 1887), 13; Keats's feeling for nature at the expense of his intellect collected a gaggle of responses from Swinburne in his *Complete Works,* XV, 109; Colvin in *Keats (1887);* Stoddard in his "Introduction" to *Selections . . . of A.C. Swinburne,* p. 43; and Bridges in *John Keats, A Critical Study,* p. 90. Three other responses, Owen in *John Keats: A Study,*p. 21; Masson in another comment in *WS&K,* p. 66; and Scherer in "Wordsworth and Modern Poetry in England," p. 192.

[29] For more on Herder's "growth, bloom, and decay" of civilizations, see Clark's *Herder: His Life and Thought* (1955) and Neff's *The Poetry of History* (1947), pp. 64-78. Both accounts are in English; both scholars' object of inquiry is Herder's *Thoughts on History* (1784-1791).

[30] With reluctance yet relief, I yield to you, and to posterity, Tabbs' poem "Keats" in *Poems.* Boston (1894).

> Upon thy tomb 'tis graven, "Here lies one
> Whose name is writ in water." Could there be
> A flight of fancy fitlier feigned for thee,
> A fairer motto for her favorite son?
> For, as the wave, thy varying numbers run—
> Now crested proud in tidal majesty,
> Now tranquil as the twilight reverie
> Of some dim lake the white moon looks upon
> While teems the world with silence. Even there,
> In each Protean rainbow-tint that stains
> The breathing canvas of the atmosphere,
> We read an exhalation of thy strains,
> Thus on the scroll of nature, everywhere,
> Thy name, a deathless syllable, remains.

[31] See Beach's "The Forms of Nature" in *The Concept of Nature in the Nineteenth Century,* pp. 31-44 for the beginnings of an account of nature's "countryside" appeal to man. Evidence listed here are Cowper's *The Task* (1785); Beattie's *The Minstrel,* Book I (1768); Wordsworth's *Tintern Abbey* (1798), *The Prelude* (1805), and *The Excursion* (1814); and Coleridge's "To the Nightingale" (1795). I add two other Coleridge poems, "To the River Otter (?1793) and "Life" (1789).

[32] See F.W.J. Schelling's *Ideen zu einer Philosophie der Natur (Ideas for a Philosophy of Nature,* 1797); Friedrich Hardenberg's (Novalis') *Hymnen an die Nacht (Hymns to the Night,* 1800), and Friedrich Holderlin's "Soul of Nature" for important leads to what today seems a remarkable thesis, nature's sacredness. Along with these Germans is another, Goethe, and two English poets Cowper and Blake, who provided 18th-century ballast to Schelling and perhaps Novalis. Then Rousseau cannot be eliminated from the group; he found nature for too long and too well to be the Great Protector and Healer of his civilization's discomforts (Neff, in *Rev.* p. 161, has supplied the titles for this f.n.).

[33] *Wordsworth, Coleridge, Emerson, and Carlyle.* Summed up in a word expressive of them more than any other: transcendentalists. Rooted in God as the source, with nature and man as God's display of the source, the views of the four writers from 1802 on strongly relate on the subject of God and Nature. With Wordsworth and Carlyle leaning toward Nature and Coleridge and Emerson toward God, they struck common ground in the fact that they had found lodestones that would enter their interpretations of a nature on display as God's work.

[34] See Blake's "Introduction," "The Lamb," and "Spring" in *Songs of Innocence* (1789), for ready pick-ups on the lamb and the child. Available in *English Romantic Writers.* Edited by David Perkins. New York: Harcourt, Brace (1967), pp. 50-53.

[35] Representative essays of Emerson on God and Nature are "Spiritual Laws," "Education," and "The Poet." In *Ralph Waldo Emerson Essays and Lectures.* Edited by Joel Porte. New York: Literary Classics of the United States (1983).

[36] For extraordinary unions of Nature and God, see Hopkins' *The Wreck of the Deutschland,* "Hurrahing in Harvest," "Pied Beauty," and "The Windhover." In Gardner's edition of *Poems of Gerard Manley Hopkins.* New York: Oxford Univ. Press (1948).

[37] For reports on Keats's "Victorian" way with nature, see

Gilfillan's "Victorian" *Gallery of Literary Portraits,* p. 380; Shairp's *On Poetic Interpretation of Nature,* p. 43; Francis Palgrave's "Notes" in *The Poetical Works of John Keats.* London (1885), p. 262; W.T. Arnold's "Introduction" in *The Poetical Works of John Keats.* London (1924), xvii; and Matthew Arnold's *On the Study of Celtic Poetry.* New York (1883), pp. 125-126.

[38] For Keats's comparison of life to a "Mansion of Many Apartments," including an "infant chamber of thoughtlessness" and a "Chamber of Maiden-Thought" . . . full of "Pain, Sickness, and Oppression," see his letter to J.H. Reynolds, 3 May 1818 *(Rollins,* ed. *Letters,* I, 280-281). Without emphasizing the fact, Owen and Bridges seem aware of Keats's growth from infant to maiden chamber in their explications of *Endymion.*

[39] Robert Bridges, *Collected Essays, Papers etc: A Critical Introduction to Keats.* London: Oxford Univ. Press (1929). IV, 129.

[40] Tennyson, Swinburne, and Arnold are explicit about man's separation from nature, to which Hardy would add: also from God. See Tennyson's *In Memoriam,* Arnold's "Quiet Work," and Hardy's *The Dynasts* and "Discouragement" for important examples of the separation; also, Swinburne's "The Launch of the Livadia," "March: An Ode," and "A Nympholept."

[41] Nature had lost a fervent follower in Goethe as early as the 1780's, when Goethe became aware of nature's contradictions. By the 1800's Wordsworth and Coleridge had become doubtful about nature's devotion to man, and by 1816 Shelley had begun to reflect nature off of Plato's stabilizing glass. Keats's reference of humanity to nature then seems natural, indeed as inevitable a nature entry as its contradiction at another stage, nature preferable to humankind.

[42] Wordsworth's "Elegiac Stanzas," "Elegiac Verses," and "To the Daisy," all 1805 poems, supply evidence of a major change in Wordsworth toward nature. Coleridge's "Dejection: An Ode" (1802) supplies major awareness by the poet of the abrasions and awesomeness of a nature become storm.

PART II:

POET

CHAPTER THREE

Keats's Victorian Apostleship

"To every man, worthy of the name of poet, the first object is always the Beautiful."[1] Arthur Hallam's remark on beauty, a reprimand to Gabriele Rossetti for his study of Dante's politics, could have occurred to Hallam from reading Tennyson or from talking with other Cambridge Apostles. The idea was almost duplicated by Swinburne in his essay "William Blake" and it could have been written by Keats in a letter, say, to Reynolds, to Woodhouse, or to George Keats. Baudelaire's remark in the 1850's, then, but embellishes a role of beauty already recognized and reverenced by Gabriele Rossetti's son, Dante Gabriel. Said Baudelaire, reverentially enough:

> *La beaute est une qualite si forte qu'elle ne peut qu'ennoblir les ames.*

In France, the sentiment constituted a renewal of romanticism shortly to become symbolic. In England, the sentiment signified the arrival of Keats to high office, his Victorian apostleship in beauty. This apostleship is my subject.

In Puritan Boston, 1854, James Russell Lowell clarified a kind of beauty that Whistler would have mentioned in 1882 had he been writing about poems instead of about pictures, and that Mallarme and Dante Gabriel Rossetti would have accepted from Whistler in that year with little change. "Keats," said Lowell, "has an instinct for fine words, which are in themselves pictures and ideas, and had more of the power of poetic expression than any modern English poet."[2] Lowell's estimate makes beauty lie beneath the surface, which is the way the Victorians would have beauty be present. To Monckton

Milnes, Sidney Colvin, and Robert Bridges, for instance, beauty could be found in beautiful words, striking images, or brocaded thoughts.[3] To Walter Bagehot, Francis Palgrave, and W.T. Arnold, it could be found in an ornate style,[4] or created in a vivid communication to the senses.[5] Beauty might be no more than the effect of a verbal picture—the hold of the supernatural, said Dante Gabriel about Keats;[6] to Walter Pater the picture should have a gem's purity and fire.[7] To the romantics, Keats' poetry had been beautiful because it was pleasurable; to the Victorians his poetry was pleasurable because it was beautiful. The Victorians had accepted the aim of poetry to please, prescribed by Wordsworth[8] and Coleridge;[9] but after 1850, were sponsoring a related aim, to create beauty, which is that of Keats.[10]

The Victorians associated Keats with beauty in three ways: as a Pre-Raphaelite, a Grecian poet, and a pure artist. Of the three, Keats as a Pre-Raphaelite was the earliest and became the most prominent identification. Even at the end of the century the image prevailed, although pure art from the Continent—*l'art pour l'art*—was obviously consolidating its hold upon the Island.[11]

A more durable identification was the Victorians' connection of Keats with Greek beauty. Best presented by Colvin[12] and Bridges,[13] Keats, Platonic in thought, gained acceptance after the Victorians' confirmation of Keats as intelligent, about 1875. Thereafter, Keats as a neo-Platonist became the most intellectual portrait of the poet created by the Victorians[14] and his Grecian rendering of nature through personification and myth, one of their most popular subjects.[15] Better than the Pre-Raphaelite image, the Victorians' identification of Keats as Grecian has survived well into the mid-twentieth century.[16]

The last, latest, but not least important Victorian impression of Keats as a poet of beauty was as a pure artist. English ancestors of Keats the pure artist are the Pre-Raphaelites; spiritual elders include the French Parnassians and Symbolistes. By the description, Keats wrote with a feeling for the tone, harmony, and form of a poem; he had then a sense of art. A paradox in literary aesthetics is that while Poe acknowledged Keats[17] and Baudelaire acknowledged Poe,[18] Baudelaire had nothing to say about Keats.[19]

Regardless, topping the aesthetic blur and the petty inconsistencies is the fact that from Kant on through Goethe, Wordsworth, Coleridge, and Shelley,[20] a living tradition of beauty served the Victorian in reading Keats. Thus Victorian writers like Dante Gabriel Rossetti, Algernon Swinburne, William Morris, and Oscar Wilde; Monckton Milnes, John Ruskin, Matthew Arnold, and William Michael Rossetti; and painters like Holman Hunt, J.E. Millais, Edward Burne-Jones, and James McNeil Whistler were drawn into the tradition in the felt way of receiving an inspiriting ideal.[21] This ideal, whether garbed as Pre-Raphaelitism, Hellenism, or art for art's sake, they honored in John Keats.

To be sure, the ideal insured a natural condition for polemics among critics, whatever their concern for poetry. Thus, the importance of Keats as a poet became second to how he exemplified, for instance, Pre-Raphaelitism or pure art. Even Leonie Villard's able handling of Keats and beauty in 1914 makes of the Romantic little more than a Pre-Raphaelite.[22] This situation exists thereafter until Middleton Murry's *Keats and Shakespeare* (1925) discloses finally a Keats whose motivation, though aesthetic in text, was Shakespearean in source. Keats's soul, said Murry, was Shakespeare's. Thus, Shakespeare had moved Keats and Keats moves us.[23]

What the critics had to say about Keats and beauty before 1880 stems from a Pre-Raphaelite source;[24] after 1880, from Arnold's, Colvin's and Mrs. Frances Owen's Hellenistic appreciation or from the late-century aesthetes' advocacy of pure art. The distinctions are important. To the Pre-Raphaelites, beauty of poetry meant beauty of word, color, or colorful word-scenes presented in a supernatural, remote, or ideal world. Medieval love, not medieval truth, was a key to this world of romance, and beauty reflected medieval love's euphoria. Critics like Swinburne, Morris, and William Michael Rossetti, concentrating on these characteristics, made Keats an earlier Pre-Raphaelite; but, also, morbid, martyred, and immature. The picture of Keats, however well received, is then that of a youth sitting among his aesthetic portraits.

By transforming Keats' beautiful words into beautiful thoughts, critics like Roden Noel and Arthur Downer could conclude that Keats had received more than a glimpse of the truth and goodness in Grecian beauty. To Matthew Arnold and Francis Palgrave, the Greek element in Keats was the adulterated Greekness in Spenser;[25] to Noel, it was Platonic;[26] to Colvin, the Keatsian Greekness, adulterated or not, was another glory to be added to a poet already idealized as Shakespearean.[27] The Victorians' likeness of Keats as Grecian added a needed dimension to their drawing of Keats as a pure artist.

The drawing of Keats as a pure artist is the creation of Pater.[28] By it Keats's poetry became art, not idea. Out of Pater's aesthetic, as from nowhere else, arose the idea of Keats the marvel of form and style.[29] But the identification, so absolute in its exclusion of thought, cheapens the praise of those who knew better the content of Keats's work. Swinburne first proclaimed the royalty of Keats as a pure artist; but Swinburne's shift from Gautier's Parnassus to Arnold's Etna[30] left later critics and poets—Wilde, Arthur Symons, W.B. Yeats, Bridges and Gerard Manley Hopkins—to represent the impression of Keats. The Pre-Raphaelites had created the cult of Keats which the followers of pure art acclaimed, then redefined. As a Pre-Raphaelite, Keats inspired the critics to a confidence in the magnitude of Keats the pure artist.

"The eager search for new sensations" is one extreme of romantic literature, according to Graham Hough; the other is the "huge nostalgia for a timeless and unchanging order."[31] Keats's attachment to medievalism illustrates both extremes; how well the Victorian critics liked them lies in their choice of *Eve of St. Agnes* and "La Belle Dame Sans Merci" as two of their five most favored poems.[32] Still, the Victorians' notion of a medieval Keats, thanks to the Pre-Raphaelites' thievery, is weak by comparison with that of a Grecian Keats. To the degree that Pre-Raphaelites like Swinburne, Dante Gabriel Rossetti, and Morris appropriated Keats's medieval subjects and his language and style, they usurped Keats's Victorian rights to the Middle Ages.[33] Along with that fact, the Pre-Raphaelites, without writing so well, wrote more medieval poetry than Keats, and their admiration of the world of Dante was as full and more conscious.[34] Finally, the Victorians, faced with the problem that Keats's medievalism could be either showy, feminine art,[35] as said Patmore and Courthope, or an illustration of Dante Gabriel Rossetti's own aesthetic interest,[36] settled on the poetry of Rossetti, then of Swinburne and Morris, to assess the medieval magic of Keats.[37] Keats, a medieval poet without obvious Pre-Raphaelite trappings, emerges at last out of De Selincourt's introduction to the *Poems of John Keats* (1905).[38]

Keats the pure artist has been better traced in the twentieth century than in the art-for-art years of the Victorian period. Nietzsche, no claimant for autonomous art, nevertheless may have had something to do with the matter, for his concept of an Apollonian art supplied to critics a depth of meaning to art for art's sake that the Victorian aesthetes were not to provide.[39]

Perhaps every Victorian critic after Carlyle read Goethe's *Faust*, but those negative to Keats did not grasp that their preference for a progressive social poetry was "Faustian." Nor did those sponsoring Keats's pure art understand that the Romantic's "To Autumn" and "Grecian Urn," for instance, either were or approached being "Apollonian." The Pre-Raphaelites were at work on an Apollonian aesthetic. The advocates of pure art achieved it in limited fashion. The critics on Keats the Grecian missed the notion completely.

Had Nietzsche been an Englishman writing at Cambridge in 1870, Pater might have kept his championship of pure art, but lost his critical crown to the better thinker. "Art is the great stimulus of life," said Nietzsche, without having read either Wordsworth or Keats; "how could it be understood as purposeless, as aimless, as *l'art pour l'art?*"[40] More important, pure art might have sponsored earlier, without loss of art, the nutrition of life which James Joyce, W.B. Yeats, and T.S. Eliot have supplied it;[41] and Keats would have attained, like them, a continental importance that he yet lacked, despite his impressive English reputation at the end of the century.

Nevertheless, Keats had survived with honors England's intention of dedicating him to beauty. As a Pre-Raphaelite, he had affirmed a beauty in life; as a Greek, a beauty in thought; as a pure artist, a beauty in art. Critics like Courthope, William Watson, and Patmore would still say in the 1890's that Keats's aesthetic glory was null, that the concept of Keats had taken him, in a sculptor's idiom, from the torso of poetry, to the head, to the pupil of an eye. An enraptured Oxford gentry was, however, to decry this view. In the sacred order of art, said Pater, then Wilde and Symons, Keats had attained his nimbus and garb. No longer initiate or adept, Keats had become beauty's very apostle.[42]

Endnotes

[1] Hallam, *The Writings of Arthur Hallam* (ed. T.H. Vail Motter), Oxford, 1943, p. 262.

[2] James Russell Lowell, *Among My Books,* Boston, 1876, p. 325.

[3] Milnes, Colvin, and Bridges found these characteristics of beauty in Keats's *Hyperion,* "Nightingale," "La Belle Dame," and "Grecian Urn."

[4] Walter Bagehot, "Pure, Ornate, and Grotesque Art in English Poetry,"*English Critical Essays, Nineteenth Century.* Ed. Edmond Jones. London, 1943, pp. 460-475.

[5] Keats's idealization of nature was "beautiful" to Milnes, Colvin, Downer, Palgrave, Noel, and W.T. Arnold.

[6] Hall Caine, *Recollections of Dante Gabriel Rossetti,* Boston, 1883, p. 167.

[7] Walter Pater, "Conclusion," *The Renaissance,* London, 1914, pp. 235-237.

[8] Wordsworth, "Preface to the Lyrical Ballads" (1800), *The Poetical Works of W.W.* Ed. by E. De Selincourt. Oxford, 1952, pp. 387, 394-5, 399-402, 404.

[9] S.T. Coleridge, *Biographia Literaria.* Ed. by J. Shawcross. Oxford, 1965. II, 10, 104, 221, 224, 307, 308.

[10] Keats, *The Letters of John Keats.* Ed. by M.B. Forman. London, 1948: To George and Thomas Keats, 28 December 1817; To Reynolds, 9 April 1818. Also, To Woodhouse, about 27 October 1818: "I feel assured that I should write from the mere yearning and fondness I have for the Beautiful, even if my night's labors should be burnt every morning, and no eye shine on them." *(The Letters of John Keats.* Ed. by Hyder Edward Rollins. Cambridge: Harvard Univ. Press, 1958. I, 388).

[11] Robert Bridges, *John Keats, A Critical Essay,* London, 1895; Arthur C. Downer, *The Odes of Keats,* Oxford, 1897; Frederic Harrison, "Lamb and Keats," *Contemporary Review* (July, 1899), pp. 62-69.

[12] Sidney Colvin, *Keats,* New York, 1887, pp. 96, 152, 153.

[13] Bridges, pp. 8-20, 33-40, 44, 55, 131-2.

[14] Frances M. Owen, *John Keats: A Study,* London, 1876, and

Roden Noel's study of Keats in *Essays on Poetry and Poets,* London, 1886, are reliable references.

[15] W.T. Arnold, Robert Bridges, Roden Noel, W.J. Courthope, and R.M. Milnes discuss Keats's role of Greek poet of nature.

[16] C.L. Finney, J.M. Murry, Paul de Ruel, Harry Levin, Stephen Larrabee, and Douglas Bush have contributed interesting twentieth-century comments on Keats's Grecian spirit.

[17] Edgar Allan Poe, *Works* (eds. Edmund C. Stedman and George E. Woodberry), Chicago, 1894, I, 60; also, *Works* (the same), 1895, VI, 121, 256. I have been guided to Poe's comments on Keats by Hyder E. Rollins in *Keats' Reputation in America to 1848,* Cambridge, Mass., 1946.

[18] See *Baudelaire on Poe* (Tr. and ed. by Lois and Francis E. Hyslop, Jr.), Pennsylvania State College: Bald Eagle Press, 1952.

[19] J.R. McGillivray's valuable bibliography of Keatsian writings indicates several scholarly and critical contributions by 19th-century French writers, but little proof comes out of them that Keats was received in France with the seriousness given him in England and the United States.

[20] Kant maintained that beauty pleases, that its pleasure is free and disinterested; that the experience of beauty is universal, subjective, associable with pleasure and pain, and an intrinsic property of objects. (See Kant, *Critique of Aesthetic Judgment,* Great Books of the Western World, XLII, 512-526.) Goethe accepted Kant's view that art has no aim outside itself, although by its own nature, it exalts the nature of man. (Kant, XLII, 546-8; also see Ruth Child, *The Aesthetics of Walter Pater,* New York, 1940, for comments on the German idealists in pure art.) Goethe also said: "A good work of art can and will have moral effects, but to demand moral aims of the artist is to ruin his craft." *(Wisdom and Experience,* tr. and ed. by Herman J. Weigand, London, 1949, p. 229). A leading statement is in Wordsworth's 1800 Preface: The poet's art "is an acknowledgment of the beauty of the universe, an acknowledgment more sincere, because not formal, but indirect. . . ." "Preface" (1800), *English Critical Essays,* p. 17. *English Critical Essays* actually contains the 1835 version of the "Preface." The differences in context are slight.

[21] George H. Ford, *Keats and the Victorians,* New Haven, 1944, has a fuller review of Keats, the Victorians, and beauty.

[22] Leonie Villard, *The Influence of Keats on Tennyson and*

Rossetti, Societe Anonyme de l'Imprimerie Mulcey Saint-Etienne, Paris, 1914, pp. 7-19.

[23] John Middleton Murry, *Keats and Shakespeare,* Oxford, 1925, pp. 3-6.

[24] Comments of Christina, William Michael, and Dante Gabriel Rossetti; Holman Hunt; Swinburne and Morris; Watts-Dunton; and Burne-Jones were valuable sources for the critics.

[25] Arnold, *Letters of Arnold to Clough,* p. 97; Francis Palgrave (ed.), *The Poetical Works of John Keats,* London, 1885, p. 262.

[26] Roden Noel, *Essays on Poetry and Poets,* p. 151.

[27] Colvin, *Keats,* pp. 95, 96, 105, 152, 153.

[28] Walter Pater, "Charles Lamb," *Appreciations,* London, Macmillan, p. 109.

[29] Refer in Pater's *The Renaissance* (New York: Modern Library, n.d.) to the essays "Aesthetic Poetry" and "Style," and to essays on Wordsworth, Lamb, and Merimee for what constitutes an autonomous art. Another reference: Whistler's *The Gentle Art of Making Enemies,* London, 1953.

[30] Swinburne's "Keats," *Encyclopaedia Britannica,* 1882 (included in Swinburne's *Complete Works,* XV, London, 1926), will indicate Swinburne's manifest shift from pure art to morality in art.

[31] Graham Hough, *The Last Romantics,* London, 1949, p. 119.

[32] The other three favored poems: "Nightingale," "Grecian Urn," and *Hyperion.*

[33] Representative studies revealing the Pre-Raphaelites' appropriation of Keats's medieval subjects and his language and style are: Ford, *Keats and the Victorians* (1944); Villard, *The Influence of Keats on Tennyson and Rossetti* (1914); Hill Shine, "The Influence of Keats upon Rossetti," *Englische Studien,* LXI (1926-27), pp. 192, 196; Lafourcade, Swinburne's *Hyperion,* London, 1927, pp. 55-58; N. Chatterjee, "A Comparative Study of Keats and the Pre-Raphaelite Poets," *Journal of the Department of Letters,* XXV, Calcutta University Press; and the *Quarterly Review* (CXXXII (Jan. 1872).

[34] By comparison with the enthusiasm of Dante Gabriel Rossetti, J.E. Millais, and Holman Hunt for Dante and the medieval world, Keats's own interest impresses one as accidental.

[35] Coventry Patmore, *Principle in Art,* London, 1989, p. 82. Courthope, "Keats's Place in Poetry," *National Review,* X (Sept. 1887), 14.

[36] See William Michael Rossetti's report in "Memoirs," *Dante Gabriel Rossetti, His Family Letters,* London, 1892. I.

[37] The contemporaries of Swinburne, Rossetti, and Morris needed only to value themselves highly enough as poets and Pre-Raphaelitism highly enough as an idea to shift their awareness from Keats's medieval influence upon the poets to Keats's medieval role in the making of a new Victorian aesthetic.

In the twentieth century Ford finds a similarity in Morris' pictoriality and in Keats's use of language; in the bedroom scene in Rossetti's "The Bride's Prelude" and in Keats's *St. Agnes;* and in the conception of Rossetti's "Blessed Damozel" and Keats's *Isabella.* (See *Keats and the Victorians,* 1944.) Hill Shine writes on the similarities between Rossetti and Keats in the foreboding shadow motif in "The King's Tragedy" and that in *Eve of St. Mark;* and in the stained-glass window description in "The King's Tragedy" and in *St. Agnes* (see "The Influence of Keats upon Rossetti," *Englische Studien,* LXI (1926-27). Leonie Villard finds a similarity between Rossetti's poet-lover in the *House of Life* and Keats's Porphyro in *St. Agnes'* and between the queen in "The King's Tragedy" and Keats's Isabella. She believes the picture work in the "Blessed Damozel" and "The Bride's Prelude" are Keatsian, and the archaic medieval effect of compound words in "St. Agnes" appear in the *House of Life* (see *The Influence of Keats on Tennyson and Rossetti,* 1914). Georges Lafourcade finds Keats's epithets in Swinburne's "The Triumph of Gloriana"; his metrics in Swinburne's "Unhappy Revenge"; and suggestions of Keats through the Pre-Raphaelites in Swinburne's "Rudel," "Lancelot," and "The Two Knights" (see *Swinburne's Hyperion and Other Poems,* 1927). Such correspondences must have saturated the Victorian reader of poetry, so much closer to the Pre-Raphaelite scene.

[38] Ernest De Selincourt, "Introduction," *The Poems of John Keats* (7th ed.), London, 1951, pp. liv, lvii.

[39] Friedrich Nietzsche, "Die Geburt der Tragodie," *Werke,* Leipzig, 1917, I, 19-34. *(The Birth of Tragedy,* tr. William A. Hausmann, London, 1909, pp. 21-37).

[40] Nietzsche, "Gotter-Dammerung," *Werke,* Leipzig, 1919, VIII, 135-6 *(The Twilight of the Idols,* tr. Anthony M. Ludovic, Edinburgh, 1915, p. 80.)

[41] See James Joyce's "The Dead," "Counterparts," *Portrait of*

an Artist as a Young Man, and *Ulysses;* W.B. Yeats' "September, 1913," "Easter, 1916," "Leda and the Swan," "Sailing to Byzantium," "The Second Coming," and "Among School Children"; and T.S. Eliot's "Gerontion," "The Hollow Men," "Ash-Wednesday," and "Burnt Norton."

The writings illustrate the completed union of a context, social and human, with its form; and outweigh the artcraft of Verlaine, Dowson, Symons, O'Shaughnessey, and the early Yeats on pain, maidens, Ireland, dreams, and art.

[42] "Keats's Victorian Apostleship" represents a reduction with relevant changes and additions of three chapters in my *Keats and the Critics, 1848-1900* (Salzburg: Universitat Salzburg, 1972), namely those concerning Keats as Pre-Raphaelite, as Grecian Poet, and as Pure Artist, pp. 163-234.

CHAPTER FOUR

Wordsworth and Keats: Empiricists

In the 20th century, with empiricism in and aesthetics somewhere else, it is difficult to realize that empiricism could have influenced two Romantic poets who would have declared themselves non-empiricists, if anything, and did consider themselves different from each other. I refer to a poet of nature, William Wordsworth, and a poet of beauty, John Keats. Nevertheless, Wordsworth and Keats came together as empiricists, linked by an unchallengeably empirical resource: associationism. My intention is to present this resource of Wordsworth and Keats and to note its presence in their poems.

John Locke introduced associationism to us all. In his celebrated rejection of innate ideas, Locke took all knowledge as originating in the senses, and thereafter evolving by associations into ideas.[1] Locke furthermore defined the three kinds of ideas constituting knowledge; in ascending order, they were ideas of sensation,[2] ideas of reflection,[3] and ideas of intellectual power. The latter were complex in nature,[4] and corresponded in both altitude and kind to ideas generated by *verstehen*, Kant's referent for higher reason.

Berkeley and Hume followed Locke's pattern of knowledge, and like him took associations as the connecting element. "Sense at first besets and overbears the mind," said Berkeley. Then "intellect begins to dawn" and "we perceive unity, identity, and existence." Thereafter, added Berkeley, the intellect grows, and "things that before seemed to constitute the Whole of Being"—sensations could be "things"—prove to be but "fleeting phantoms."[5]

Said Hume: Perceptions of the mind divide into two classes, each determined by its force and vivacity. Less "forcible and lively" perceptions, according to Hume, are *"Thoughts, or Ideas."* More lively and forcible—since associable with what one feels, hears, loves,

79

hates, desires, and wills—are *Impressions*. To Hume, "impressions," a catch-all word here, could be another word for sensations.[6]

One doubts that Wordsworth and Keats would have picked up the suggestions of associationism in the epistemologies of Locke, Berkeley, and Hume. Indeed, if the poets had, they would have been spending more time on dissecting the mind and defining knowledge than on writing associational poetry. The fact is, however, the two poets did not have to bother: a fourth empiricist, David Hartley, had already characterized what went on in the movement from sensation to idea. Hartley called what went on *associationism*. Without either Wordsworth's or Keats's acknowledgement of debt, Hartley was to identify how they thought in a considerable number of their poems.

Locke had said that sensations become ideas by a complex and subtle pattern of associations lodged in the "mind's reflection." Thus "when the understanding is once stored up with these simple ideas, it has the power to repeat, compare, and unite them, even to an almost infinite variety. . . ." Nevertheless, the mind will collect its associations, he had added, in a predictable pattern.[7] Hartley's addendum was to formulate that pattern—to a fine edge, as it were—in terms of what he calls the "passions." Thus, said Hartley, if sensations constitute the beginning of what is to become idea, sensations will generate the imagination, and sensation and imagination (together) will generate ambition. Ambition, in turn, added to the processing, will generate self-interest, and these together generate sympathy; and sympathy added will help to generate high pleasure and pain—or theopathy, according to Hartley; and theopathy added will generate a moral sense—the ultimate faculty in Hartley's arrangement of the mind, and a height, one can assume, from which one may descend back to the fingers and the nose and the eyes for more sensations. Such an accretion and range, Hartley added, creates a complexity that makes one's analysis of the passions difficult.[8] I should add that Hartley's particular computerizing makes our comprehension of the mind very, very difficult. Nevertheless, Hartley has explained a complex but realistic movement of human response from sensation to emotion to thought to morality and back. The elements represent no more than ordinary needs of man in defining experience; they represented not less than primal needs of Wordsworth and Keats in writing poems. The remainder of this paper will evidence this Wordsworthian and Keatsian fact.

First, Wordsworth:

Wordsworth knew of Hartley's associations through Coleridge. One could not need, however, Coleridge's attestation to know that Wordsworth had been associational in his 1800 *Preface*. Our feelings, said Wordsworth, are "modified and directed" by our thoughts, "the representatives of all our feelings." Thereafter, by contemplating the relation of these feelings, "we discover what is really important to man and so . . . by repetition and continuation of thought, our feelings become connected with important subjects." Obeying such impulses and habits, added Wordsworth, "causes one not only to describe objects, but also to connect them." Thus one becomes "enlightened' in thought and "strengthened and purified" in "affections."[9]

Tintern Abbey (1798) reveals what Wordsworth had in mind even before writing the *Preface*. Wordsworth recalls to the reader that, though five years absent from the countryside—a good locale to get the senses associating—he has retained nature's "beauteous forms," and has received not only "sensations sweet," but also emotions in the heart and tranquility in the mind. Furthermore, his memory of nature has inspired him to "unremembered acts/Of kindness and of love." Not least, his memory of nature has helped him out of his feeling of the burden and mystery of his world into a "blessed mood" *(TA,* 22-42). Wordsworth has, at the River Wye, gone from sensations before nature to imagination to a rapport with humankind; then into a high pleasure from "acts of love"—theopathy; then into a moral sensing of being blest. A serendipity: the experience has been epiphanic; the poet has been enabled to "see into the life of things." *(TA,* 48)

In later lines, Wordsworth repeats this associational pattern. Having sensed in nature a sublimity and presence beyond nature, he is impelled to conclude that he is

> still
> A lover of the meadows and the woods
> And mountains. . . well pleased to recognize
> In nature and the language of the sense
> The anchor of my present thoughts, the nurse,
> The guide, the guardian of my heart, and soul
> Of all my moral being.
>
> *(TA,* 102-104; 107-111)

The revelation confirms the intimation that his sister Dorothy, with him at the Wye, will receive a similar beatification as she grows up.

"Therefore"—Wordsworth to Dorothy—

> . . . let the moon
> Shine on thee in thy solitary walk;
> And let the misty mountain-winds be free
> To blow against thee, and, in after years,
> When these wild ecstasies shall be matured
> In a sober pleasure; when thy mind
> Shall be a mansion for all lovely forms,
> Thy memory be a dwelling place
> For all sweet sounds and harmonies; oh! then
> If solitude, or fear, or pain, or grief,
> Should be thy portion, with what healing thoughts
> Of tender joy wilt thou remember me. . . .
>
> *(TA,* 134-145)

What is true, association-wise, in *Tintern Abbey* can be argued for in the *Ode on Intimations of Immortality* (1806). The first four stanzas of the poem, for instance, express Wordsworth's loss of nature's glory, the poet's recapture, then his loss of the glory again *(OII,* 1-57). They illustrate how stages of sensation and imagination are wrought before a nature experience.

The next stanzas intensify the feelings of loss by describing how one grows out of sensings of nature's heaven-sent glory felt in "childhood joys" into custom's adult weight: a dulling experience associable with sympathy's loss and apathy's pain *(OII,* 77-127). Then, in a climacteric, Wordsworth resolves what has been lost of nature into what can be recalled or imagined. Thanks to his imagination, for instance, he can recreate childhood scenes supposed to have been lost; thanks to a maturing "philosophic mind," he can conclude that what he has lost of nature is less than what he has gained. Thus he continues his celebration *(OII,* 128-129). That a high pleasure is being reconstituted in nature would seem self-evident.

One can trace these associational hijinks of Wordsworth beyond *Tintern Abbey* and *Immortality Ode* into "Expostulation and Reply" (1798), *Resolution and Independence* (1802), *The Prelude* (1798-1850), "Elegiac Stanzas" (1805), and *The Excursion* (1814).[10] In each instance, nature or someone or something in nature is Wordsworth's catalyst; there follow sense-reports that gather in "spontaneous overflow," and lead to recollections "in tranquility."

The associational process is prominent moreover in "The Solitary Reaper" (1803) and "I wandered lonely as a cloud" (1804) to illustrate the poet's way of writing a poem; in *The River Duddon* (1820) to illustrate his shifts from naturalist to historian to philosopher; or in "Ode to Duty" (1805), where nature is no longer a catalyst, to illustrate his shift from sensation to moral sense.[11]

My conclusion is that, throughout his long career with words, Wordsworth beheld what he saw first through the senses, thereafter through the mind. If he became a transcendentalist in parts of the *Immortality Ode,*[12] and at the end of *The River Duddon,*[13] his upreach to oversoul followed a report from his senses. He was then an associationist—an empiricist—from beginning to end in his poetry, and never a Cartesian rationalist like Alexander Pope in *Essay on Man,*[14] and only occasionally a Kantian *a priori-ist,*[15] despite transcendental leanings well-rooted in him by 1805. Wordsworth's posture before experience then convicts him of having been born in the right place, at the right time, and with the right complication of vistas, philosophy, and muse's genes to become a successful empirical poet. The wonder is that he did not also effect the aesthetic that none of the 18th-century empiricists was to provide and that the 1800 *Preface* merely predicted.[16]

Now, Keats.

James Ralston Caldwell said in *Keats's Fancy* that "the intellectual identity of a poet . . . consists in how, more than in what, he thinks."[17] This Arnoldian bit of wisdom allows for the distinction of poet as artist from poet as ideologist, and accounts for the fact that a poet-artist can make a dullest platitude come alive by his art while a poet-moralist can kill a living judgment by his preaching. The above differentiation brings me to the gist of this introduction: That Keats must be seen as empiricist, but as an artist transforming the associationist's way of looking at things rather than as an ideologist like Wordsworth placing his material along, for instance, a Hartleian slant.[18]

Evidences of Keats's by-play with associationism loom in his letters.[19] In May 3, 1818, for instance, he wrote John Hamilton Reynolds:

> . . . This crossing a letter is not without its association—for chequer work leads us naturally to a milk maid, milk maid to Hogarth, Hogarth to Shakespeare, Shakespeare to Hazlitt, Hazlitt to Shakespeare—and thus by pulling an apron string we set a pretty peal of chimes at work.[20]

In October, 1818, he wrote to George and Georgianna Keats:

> The roaming of the wind is my wife, and the Stars through
> the windowpane are my Children. . . . I feel more and
> more everyday, as my imagination strengthens, that I do
> not live in this world alone, but in a thousand worlds. . .
> I am with Achilles standing in the Trenches, or with
> Theocritus in the Vales of Sicily. Or I throw my whole
> being into Troilus. . . .[21]

The imagination is the particular manifestation of the mind in
these letters. A year earlier, in a now-famous letter to Benjamin Bailey,
November 22, 1817, Keats had articulated another activity of the
imagination, its capacity to recall.

> But as I was saying—the simple Imaginative Mind may
> have its rewards in the repetition of its own silent Working
> coming continually on the Spirit with a fine Suddenness—
> to compare great things with small—have you never . .
> . fe[l]t over again your very Speculations and Surmises
> at the time it first operated on your Soul—[22]

Keats continues on in his letter to introduce sensation, thought, the
mind, and—something nudges me—a Westmoreland-oriented bard.
List ye.

> What a time! I am continually running away from the
> subject—sure this cannot be exactly the case with a
> Complex Mind—. . . (one that) would exist partly on
> Sensation, partly on Thought—to whom it is necessary
> that years should bring the philosophic mind—. . . .[23]

Keats's most evident use of associationism appears in his early
poems. "How many bards gild the lapses of time" (1816) and "The
Poet" (1816) illustrate this tendency in the early sonnets and "I stood
tip-toe" and *Sleep and Poetry* (1816) in the early long poems. In
"How many bards," for instance, an associationism occurs on four
of the levels enumerated by Hartley. In the octave, sensation and
thought and pleasure occur. Thus, says Keats, "how many bards"
have gilded his reading hours. They have so delighted him, he adds,
that he has brooded "over their beauties," receiving "throngs of
thoughts," even feeling their "pleasing chime."

In the sestet occur sensations at first, with imagination following, and pleasure at the end. This time the sensations are from nature's sounds and a bell; thus,

> The songs of birds—the whispering of leaves—
> The voice of waters—the great bell that heaves.
> With solemn sound—and thousand others more. . .
>
> (ll. 10-12)

Now nature has been added to poet as a source of "pleasing chime" in Keats.

In the poem Keats has found two ways of receiving a "chime." In the octave the way is explicit, Wordsworthian: certain poets, Keats says, turn him on. In the sestet, on the other hand, the way is evocative, Keatsian; for however explicit the individual sounds of nature, for instance, they combine within Keats to induce another "chime." Call it listenable chime. Implied is a natural rapture.

Both octave and sestet share, thereafter, in a grand tonality: the authentic Longinian "chime" of the whole poem. For, whatever its difference in topic and approach, the poem has fused to intensify the aesthetic chime begun in the sestet. It is a paradoxical achievement of high pleasure for the reader, I shall add, then say that Wordsworth does the same in "I wandered lonely as a cloud" (1804), "To a Cuckoo" (1804), and "To a Highland Girl" (1803); and Keats in "The Grasshopper and Cricket" (1816) and "Ode on Melancholy" (1819). On the other hand, "The Poet," however auspicious its subject, is patterned by Keats in simple associations.

> At morn, at noon, at eve, and middle night
>   He passes forth into the charmed air,
>   With talisman to call up spirits rare
> From plant, cave, rock, and fountain—To his sight
> The hush of natural objects opens quite
>   To the core: and every secret essence there
>   Reveals the elements of good and fair;
> Making him see where learning hath no light.
> Sometimes above the gross and palpable things
>   Of this diurnal ball, his spirit flies
>   On awful wing; and with its destined skies
> Hold premature and mystic communings:
>   Till such unearthly intercourses shed
>   A visible halo round his mortal head.

85

Caldwell's thoughts on this poem could as well be mine:

> . . . (T)he poet is stimulated by an experience in nature. He can by a special gift derive much more than mere sensations—even abstract ideas of goodness and beauty—and much more than is permitted to the learned mind . . . (for) sometimes he is borne far away from the sensory experience to a sense of eternal verities.[24]

Thus, from experiencing nature to seeing verities: the development is from sensation to thought, and from responses of sympathy, past pleasure and pain, to intimations of moral sense.

"I stood tip-toe upon a little hill," a poem of associations, is concerned to describe sensations from nature. *Sleep and Poetry,* equally concerned, is also Keats's pastiche of what it takes to write a poem. Beginning with sensorials, *Sleep and Poetry* develops into a celebration of the imagination, a repudiation of Boileau and the couplet, an extollment of books and sleep as a means to poetry, and the necessity of friends, a little sweat, and ten years to strike a poetic lode. Keats's associationism in *Sleep and Poetry* has brought the poet out of sensation and imagination into intellect and theopathy, the widest range of evocations Keats achieves among his early poems.

In both poems Keats leaps from subject to subject and from image to image to bring off nevertheless a communicable meaning and effect.[25] I select an example from *Sleep and Poetry:*

> Stop and consider! life is but a day;
> A fragile dew-drop on its perilous way
> From a tree's summit; a poor Indian's sleep
> While his boat hastens to the monstrous steep
> of Montmorenci. Why so sad a moan?
> Life is the rose's hope while yet unblown;
> The reading of an everchanging tale;
> The light uplifting of a maiden's veil;
> A pigeon tumbling in clear summer air;
> A laughing school-boy, without grief or care,
> Riding the springy branches of an elm.

(85-95)

Life then is an association or five, plus a day, plus a sensation or three, plus a muse's gift that Aristotle made into poetic mandate: the ability to think in metaphors.

86

As the quotation suggests, the imagination is prominent in the poems. In "I stood tip-toe" Keats has a poet, turned on by his recall of Narcissus and Echo, bring shapes and songs to a "wanderer by moonlight" . . .

> Shapes from the invisible world, unearthly singing
> From out the middle air, from flowing nests,
> And from the billowy silkiness that rests
> Full in the speculation of the stars.

(186-189)

At poem's end, Keats brings a halt to at least his flight-work:

> —. . . no more,
> My wandering spirit must no further soar. —

(241-242)

In *Sleep and Poetry,* the sun-charioteer—the imagination—prompts the poet into a question:

> Is there so small a range
> In the strength of manhood, that the high
> Imagination cannot freely fly
> As she was wont...?

(163-166)

The image and question suggest Keats's thesis, like Kant's and Hume's in their contexts,[26] that the imagination is the faculty (along with the will) for transferring nature from sensation to idea, from simple existence to complex reflection. I would not nag, yet must remind you that this process of the imagination is associational.

The case would stand for Keats, empiricist, were one to go no further with his poems, and indeed in this chapter I shall go little further. I shall call your attention to the fact that *The Eve of St. Agnes* (1819) goes in plot from sensation to imagination to pleasure, then back to sensation; "To Autumn" (1819), save for the Gleaner personification, goes from sensation to sensation with deepening intensity; and "Grecian Urn" (1819) goes from sensations of sight and sound to thoughts on beauty and truth to, perhaps, moral sense when Keats concludes

> That is all
> Ye know on earth, and all ye need to know,

Finally, "Ode to a Nightingale" (1819) is all sensation and imagination until Keats has "become a clod," whereupon the poem becomes thought and pleasure, then reverses with the twice-said "forlorn" to pain. One could carry this argument of parallels into *Hyperion* (1818-1819), *The Fall of Hyperion* (1819), and "La Belle Dame Sans Merci" (1819).

I recommend then that one accept both Wordsworth and Keats as empiricists, however transcendental Wordsworth could become and however enamored of beauty Keats was. But having set up this postulate, I must add that the poets' associationism represents no guarantee that their poetry is well-written or profound. It does offer the promise that their poetry will be plausible, their detail concrete, and their method, however different, ranging and full.

Wordsworth's use of associationism was, of course, more conscious than Keats's. In *Tintern Abbey,* the great *Ode,* and the occasionally great *Prelude,* Wordsworth used associationism simply to explain his debt to nature. In our shift from nature, Wordsworth's debt seems an act of will, more appreciated by Mr. W.'s age than by ours. On the other hand, Keats used associations in nature to achieve art. In *Sleep and Poetry,* for instance, he used nature to describe constituents of poetry, and in *Hyperion* he personified nature to vivify an astonishing principle of survival.

John Middleton Murry used the word "sacramental" to describe Wordsworth's way of writing within a system; "liturgical" to explain Keats's use of a system to construe a world.[27] The distinction is between an ideologist making dogma out of a source and an aesthete creating "felt beauty" whatever its source—an urn, a bird, or a knight or a wight. The difference may make Keats more palatable than Wordsworth for 20th-century taste; it may prove to make Keats more palatable for after-centuries. Regardless, the distinction will not dispel Keats's commonalty with Wordsworth in the associational experience. Both poets belonged to an age that decreed that they think thus, and they did so without real dissent. They then fulfilled in poetry what the philosophers were not able to supply in aesthetic theory. Had the philosophers done so, you may be sure that I would never have built up the adrenalin required to write this paper.

Endnotes

[1] Associationism hardly died with its 18th-Century parentage. Rather, it has survived as an unquoted referent in modern forms of pragmatism as well as in John Dewey's *Art as Experience,* I. A. Richards' *Principles of Literary Criticism,* and Charles Morris' *Signs, Language, and Behavior.* Associationism as aesthetic terminology, however, has been superseded by modern modes of criticism emanating from Aristotle, Coleridge, and Eliot. These modes make works of art their concern and tend toward structural and organic analysis rather than associational. Both the New and the Chicago Critics as well as Yvor Winters and R. P. Blackmur illustrate this 20th-century development; also, Harold Bloom and Noam Chomsky.

[2] John Locke, *Essay on the Human Understanding* (Philadelphia, 1856), Chapter II, Sec. 2, pp. 84-85.

[3] Locke, Chap. VI, p. 90.

[4] Locke, Chap. XII, p. 110.

[5] George Berkeley, *Essays, Principles, Dialogues,* ed. by Mary Whiton Calkins (New York, 1929), Sec. 294, pp. 419-420.

[6] David Hume, *An Enquiry Concerning Human Understanding* (Chicago, 1900), Chap. II, p. 15.

[7] Locke, Chap. II, pp. 83-84.

[8] *Hartley on the Mind, with Essays Relative to it by Joseph Priestley* (London, 1790). The Hartley reference is from *Observations on Man,* included in the above work. The reference is Proposition LXI, pp. 202-203 of *Hartley on the Mind.*

[9] Wordsworth's use of empiricist doctrine has been briefly treated by Claude L. Finney, *The Evolution of Keats's Poetry,* I, 239-240; more fully by Arthur Beatty in *William Wordsworth: His Doctrine and Art in Their Historical Relation* (see Chaps. III, IV); also by A. E. Powell in *The Romantic Theory of Poetry;* by Joseph Warren Beach in *The Concept of Nature in Nineteenth-Century English Poetry,* S. F. Gingerich in *Essays in the Romantic Poets,* Hoxie Neale Fairchild in *The Romantic Quest,* and Newton P. Stallknecht in *Strange Seas of Thought.* I should add that the last four scholars, while noting Wordsworth's empirical turn, regard Wordsworth as a transcendental poet. One last reference which must be included: Ernest De Selincourt in his introduction to the Oxford Edition of Wordsworth's *The Prelude* (1805).

[10] *Resolution and Independence* is associational in the relationship between Wordsworth and the leech-gatherer, and between the leech-gatherer and the leech. The first five books of *The Prelude* are highly associational. "Elegiac Stanzas" is associational in the relationship between Wordsworth and Peele Castle during a storm and during a calm. Like *The Prelude, The Excursion* can be associational almost anywhere in the poem. These examples could be expanded in depth and complexity in a longer footnote.

[11] All of "The Solitary Reaper" and "I wandered lonely as a cloud" are associational in method. *The River Duddon* is associational particularly in its nature descriptions, but the changes of persona by Wordsworth in the *Duddon* illustrate development via associations. The "Ode to Duty" may be emphasized as transcendental in its *a priori* emphasis on "duty" in the new Wordsworth. Still, Stanza 3, a review of what Wordsworth was as nature's son, follows an associational pattern.

[12] I cite as transcendental Stanza 5 in the *Immortality Ode,* where Wordsworth acknowledged God, not nature, as the *a priori* source of man's joy in nature. Argument could be made also for Stanzas 6, 7, and 8 as representing transcendental verse. I, however, regard them as *a posteriori* evidence of a child's growth into adulthood.

[13] See "After-thought," the last sonnet in *The River Duddon.*

[14] Alexander Pope argues in the *Essay on Man* from thesis to proof throughout that long poem. Descartes recommends the procedure in *Discourse on Method* as a way of preparing exhaustive categories of knowledge on a topic.

[15] See f.n. 12 for a Wordsworthian example.

[16] The 18th-century empiricists were to become 19th-Century utilitarians, concerned with social, legal, and economic reform, not with beauty and art. These interests, in the wake of the American and French Revolutions, left their imprint upon Wordsworth despite his nature leanings. Also, Wordsworth gives full evidence in many, many poems that nature is far larger than art—than aesthetics, then, if a choice had to be made.

[17] Caldwell, *Keats's Fancy* (Ithaca, 1945), p. 3.

[18] See Caldwell, p. 7, for the Keatsian side of this critical view.

[19] Associationism is characteristic of letters of Byron and Shelley as well as of Keats. Caldwell explains for all three in explaining Keats: "(His) psychology was the psychology of the

association of ideas." (Caldwell, p. 8)

[20] *The Letters of John Keats,* ed. by M. B. Forman (Oxford, 1931), I, 155.

[21] *Letters,* I, 261.

[22] *Letters,* I, 73-74.

[23] *Ibid.* A letter to Reynolds on February 19, 1818, uses a spider image to describe the associational work of the imagination. Leigh Hunt and William Hazlitt, Keats's friends, respectively use associationism in comments in the *Round Table* (1815-1817) by Hunt, and by Hazlitt in *An Essay on the Principles of Human Action, to which are added Some Remarks on the Systems of Hartley and Helvetius* (1805)—a suggestion as to how generally the term was used seventy-five years after its formalizing by Hartley.

[24] Caldwell, p. 11. Miriam Allott questions whether "The Poet" is Keats's; Mabel Steele and Jack Stillinger say it is John Taylor's. Whatever, "The Poet" remains Keatsian in language, form, and associations.

[25] Keats's method of associations here is exceptional, rather than typical. See "On Seeing the Elgin Marbles," "After Dark Vapours," and "Epistle to My Brother George" for typical examples.

[26] See Kant, *Critique of Judgement* and Hume, *Essay Concerning Human Understanding* for the philosophic structuring of the human mind.

[27] Murry, *Studies in Keats, New and Old* (London, 1939), p. 143. Says Murry: "There is an element of Protestant or Puritan self-assertive austerity in Wordsworth that, absent in Keats, would seem a moral weakness." Keats is content to reveal and suggest; "whereas . . . Wordsworth [is] driven to exhort and demonstrate." How ironic that what seemed Keats's moral weakness has turned out to be his aesthetic strength.

CHAPTER FIVE

Testimonial for Hayden[1]

Donald E. Hayden's *Literary Studies: The Poetic Process* reminds one of the fact that always with us are the five scholars: 1) *les géants* (star-searchers), the masters of idea and evidence like Wellek, Lovejoy, and Bate; 2) *les compendieuses* (blow-hards), related to the giants, but uncritical and, like Victorian biographers, enmeshed in facts; 3) *les idéologues (puro bandido),* the scholar as idea—turned on, turning on. Coleridge became ideologue after reading Hartley and Schelling; Arnold after reading England and self; Bentham became ideologue when *utility* outweighed him—neither weighing, however, more than a hundred pounds. Consider today Trilling and Leavis on culture, Ronald Crane on genre, and Harold Bloom on trope. Also, watch them. They are destructive, dangerous, and strong. 4) *Les textualistes* (burrowers, lynxes, lynx-eyed hawks). Coleridgean by descent, Aristotelian in stance, these are purchasers of symbols and interpreters of style. Fulfilling when concrete, epiphanic when right, they are also Allen Tate, Karl Kroeber, Geoffrey Hartman, and Laurence Perrine. Donald Hayden, I believe, does not belong in this group. Professor Hayden belongs, rather, among 5) *les tapissiers* (tapestry-makers), and with him H.W. Garrod exploring Keats's sonnets; M. R. Ridley, the *Eve of St. Agnes;* and Earl Wasserman, Keats's odes. A good *tapestere (ME, MF)* is enamored of colors, textures, and tones in the work of such poets as Keats, Tennyson, Browning, Stevens, and Pound. A tapestere can collate, explicate, and prosodize. He is, like Professor Hayden, comfortable as no other scholar within the five-to-ten-page comment, and within that limit shows proportion and completeness. His paraphrases are succinct, his secondary sources select, and his sources do not dominate his subject. This second or third among scholars is consciously precise, economical, and clear, for obscurity is a bane to him and repetition an insult. His stitchery, then, once on the wall, will be manifest but will not have taken over the arras. We hyphenate such scholars into scholar-critics. Donald Hayden, I say, is among them.

It is easy therefore for me to appreciate Professor Hayden's *Literary Studies*. Four of his writings are on Wordsworth and one writing is on Keats. It is within this cluster that his major concern, the poetic process, acquires major meaning. But this concern of Professor Hayden's carries over into less apparently related writings, for instance, his one on Thomas Mann's *Joseph and His Brethren* and his one on poets Auden, Spender, and Lewis visiting the University of Tulsa. Professor Hayden's capture of Mann's parallels between Old Testament Joseph and New Testament Christ captures also Mann's and Hayden's poetic imagination at work, and his account of C. Day Lewis's campus lecture includes Lewis's notion of the poetic process. Said Lewis (I paraphrase): "An artificer of the imagination like the poet supplies a knowledge even as the scientist employs the imagination to supply another knowledge." This correlation is profound; nor do I deepen its profundity by saying that it consolidates similar statements of Eliseo Vivas and challenges Richard McKeon and his Chicago Critics. The important fact is that it makes literature a viable knowledge, and thus rescues it from the advocates of literature as pleasure. Since Coleridge and Kant, these pleasurists have been everywhere and everybody.

A reviewer must show his negative side, otherwise he would not appear omniscient. My "omniscience" is then jolted in *Literary Studies* by Professor Hayden's "Toward a Sane Look at Censorship and Obscenity." Professor Hayden's look represents sanity itself; the difficulty is that his look does not get inside the subject. Both censorship and obscenity, for instance, affect literature, and thus its poetic process. Professor Hayden, however, does not develop this fact. Rather, beyond an effective review from three millennia back, his treatment of censorship suggests that the problem is typical and the solution at hand. Regarding obscenity, the process is the same. I would set down Professor Hayden's solutions as sops. To me, they are his light contribution to an otherwise admirable monograph.

Professor Hayden's solution for censorship is to leave it off legally, but to allow one's respect for government—a Burkean pass—to permit a "free flow" of ideas that will challenge and improve the state—a Painean catch. Then, touchdown! But, alas, no points. This solution represents what has been happening in Europe and the Americas since 1775 and is current not only in Western Europe and in Canada, Mexico, Brazil, and the United States, but also in Australia, India, Turkey, and Japan. It is the arrangement that has made censorship in the democracies a minor rather than a major problem. Professor Hayden would have scored at least a safety with this fact. But the fact would also have obviated his rendering the subject.

Professor Hayden's solution for obscenity represents a partial analysis in that he has limited his discussion to obscenity's modern tonic, *eau de pornographie*. For this compelling elixir Professor Hayden has one compelling antidote: to make the body into a "holy temple" by loving God, supporting serious studies of sex, and combatting sex-appetites in the school-hall with sex-education in the school-room. Nothing is new about this solution, and in the present everything about it may be old. Implied in Professor Hayden's antidote, for instance, is the fact that spirit is separate from matter, that spirit is to be extolled and matter deplored, and that the Bible can be trusted but the senses can not. This kind of thinking is right for the lingering Puritan or the churchly adult, but will make little address to those in the pornographic zoo. To those animals, whether in high school or college, or however "reborn" into latterday spawning, God *is* dead and matter, live; and spirit is energy rather than beatitude. For them, life represents neither goal nor dream, neither loss nor gain, but a Pavlov/Skinner conditioning. Science, art, and athletics are the great gods of these youngsters, whatever their age; technology is their religion; and the pill, drugs, and X-rated movies are their relaxations. Professor Hayden's study could be frosty stuff to them; could be as whiskery as Santa Claus, and almost as sentimental.

Inevitably we elders must blame the young for this pornographical impasse. Indeed, much of the blame should go to them, for their materialism is shallow and their ethics are shifty. But, allowing for the crash-appeal of sex, we elders are even more to blame inasmuch as we have not clarified the lightness and foolishness of pornography along with its blight. We then have not given the subject perspective. Thus, accepted is the fact that obscenities other than pornography exist, that these include cursing and profanation of man; also, the gestures and words connoting brutality, hypocrisy, lying, pandering, and betrayal. One knows, furthermore, that these obscenities differ in scope and degree and that, of the above, all except cursing are more serious than pornography. I suggest therefore that pornography may be closer to tease than overwhelment; it is then a deceit, carnal in nature, but, unless festered by perversion or prostitution, more sideshow frolic than main-tent event. Dante made carnality *(carnitas)* a lighter sin than gluttony, greed, and anger. So do the youngsters, including their dirty old men. In their world of adrenalin and spine— and yours also, understand, but not mine—"soft-core" pornography may constitute more license than infraction, and "hard-core" more licentiousness than sin. This subject is too tender for me to go any further with it. Thus, in haste, I conclude: But, I may be wrong.

Professor Hayden's "Mann's Joseph and Christ" is to me pure cameo, etched to a turn, and illustrating what Professor Hayden does best in *Literary Studies*. I go, nevertheless, to "Keats's 'Ode to Melancholy': A Study in Dialectic" to record a greater pleasure, the recognition—call it Edmund Wilson's "shock" or Aristotle's "discovery"—that in "Melancholy" has occurred a synthesis of beauty, often signified as pleasure, joy, or imagination; and of truth, as often signified as thought, sorrow, or experience. Adds Professor Hayden: The synthesis occurring in "Melancholy" was predicted in *Endymion,* lost in "Nightingale," literalized in "Grecian Urn," and evoked in "Autumn." Such a recognition has sent this reader back to Keats for another glance and hopefully another article.

However much I am indebted to Professor Hayden for these two studies, I nevertheless turn to three of his four on Wordsworth for what, to me, is his most valuable work in *Literary Studies.* In one scholarly commentary, Professor Hayden, with examples from *The Prelude,* equates Wordsworth's "spots of time" with Joycean (and Aquinian) epiphany. This equation either makes Wordsworth romantic and modern or Joyce modern and romantic, and I suspect, despite the writers' differences, it does both. In another commentary, Professor Hayden explains the blurriness in *The Borderers* as Wordsworth's own. Ridden with guilt over Annette Vallon and the French Revolution, and in midstream between Godwin and society and Coleridge and nature, Wordsworth rendered into art what he could not define as sin and crime in him. Result: a blurry Oswald, a rationalized crime, and a third-rate work of art.

A third commentary—on Wordsworth as an early ecologist— concerns me most, for the study is pivotal in a modern's appreciation of the poet. Professor Hayden's thesis is explicit: Wordsworth was an ecologist before *ecology* had been coined. Yet, two reviewers of Professor Hayden's study have deplored the assessment as a grasping at straws to make Wordsworth a modern. These charges deserve challenging for, even if they do not represent an implied verdict that Wordsworth is a "dated" romantic, they ignore the fact that romanticism is not a dated civilization and that our concepts of nature since Darwin have not shifted as radically as the two assume. Thus, if differences in the conception of nature have emerged, similarities remain, and Wordsworth can be found in either development.

To cite differences, nature to Wordsworth was larger than man; in the present, man—now nature's technocrat rather than lover—is larger than nature. Thus, if nature helped man, according to Wordsworth, today man helps nature. Diametrical shifts, it would seem, with the Wordsworthian position obsolete. Still, each relation, however shifted, implies a rapport between man and nature; in Wordsworth's instance because nature was beneficent, good, transforming, and restorative of man; in our instance, thanks to our notions about animals and birds, because man is beneficent, good, transforming, and restorative of nature.

Until his death, Wordsworth inveighed against the destruction of forests, the carelessness of tourists, and man's bungling of nature with his buildings and landscapes. Likewise, we inveigh against herbicides, pollution of streams, and smog, and, to add a couple from Wordsworth, 1835, deforestation and tourist-littering. Wordsworth, and Professor Hayden, sized up for us the fact that ecological wastage is industrial, economic in origin, with profits as catalyst and the entrepreneur (Wordsworth's lumberman) as profiteer. We moderns have not departed one jot from this canny and intense perception.

Man has been ecological about nature since the first Egyptians and Greeks and, in the modern centuries, since Petrarch's ascent of Mont Ventoux to acknowledge nature's beauty and inspiration. If Wordsworth's acknowledgment, 500 years later, is related to Petrarch's, ours, after 150 years, has not departed from Wordsworth's. Only the emphases have shifted, not the subject, and some moderns—ranchers, farmers, fishermen, bird-watchers, and bird-artists—are more Wordsworthian than modernist on the subject. I have to agree with Professor Hayden, therefore, that Wordsworth as ecologist is a subject for now and recommends Wordsworth for now; and though the subject is not as expanding or focused as

Wordsworth the epiphanist, it remains a magnitude, hence is not dismissable. For me, the subject is not even arguable.

Donald Hayden's *Literary Studies: The Poetic Process* represents, then, good scholarship—that is, firm tapestry-making, for the stitching is orderly, worked out; and, with our blinders off, the arras is there. Not anywhere has *Literary Studies* revealed the twin banes of scholarship, the misaccount or the overstatement. For me that fact is an atonement, but, then, *Literary Studies* has also been for me a learning experience.

Endnotes

[1] "Testimonial for Hayden" is a critique of Donald E. Hayden's *Literary Studies: The Poetic Process* (University of Tulsa, 1978), 75 pp. Included in the work are studies of Wordsworth and Keats.

PART THREE:

HERO

CHAPTER SIX

Napoleon Bonaparte, Noble Outlaw

I shall surprise no one by saying that Napoleon Bonaparte has become a legend since his death in 1821. I would expect to surprise no one by adding that Napoleon had become a legend in his lifetime. I expect to surprise someone, however, in saying that his legend is based on fact, is not outsize though larger than life, and is little different today from its shaping in the mid-1810's. In this chapter I would justify this last sentence of facts; also define the legend to which Napoleon belongs. The venture will keep one close to Napoleon the man; it will also trace Napoleon's change into symbol and myth. All going well, the venture will have pinpointed when the legend became living, then set; and what should occur in all is a hero's career going like rockets: quick rise to a height, then descent to the earth. I shall describe the hero at his height as *non pareil;* in his decline as *manque.*[1] Napoleon Bonaparte had become *non pareil* at 30; at 46 he had become *manque.* In becoming *manque,* Napoleon had become, by literary description, a Noble Outlaw. This Noble Outlaw will represent the ordering idea in my discussing Napoleon.

In *The Byronic Hero,* Peter Thorslev has located the Noble Outlaw as pre-Byronic, a union of the medieval and romantic ballad outlaw with the Gothic villain. Thorslev is correct, I believe, to add that the Noble Outlaw was a simple man without real sensitivity. These characteristics, however, are not Napoleon's. Thorslev also says that the Noble Outlaw possessed a passionate nature, took over in situations, seemed larger than life, was personally heroic, and dominated people and events through will, courage, and magnetism. I intend to prove that these characteristics are Napoleon's. Another characteristic, also Napoleon's, is the Noble Outlaw's capacity for leadership. During the Romantic Age, Napoleon's leadership was unquestioned and regarded as natural, innate. Schiller's Karl Moor also had this kind of leadership as well as our modern Hannibal, George Patton. Their opposite is the cool logistical leadership represented by Wellington and MacArthur.

Other characteristics of the Noble Outlaw are his personalizing of justice, speaking up on matters, dictating without appearing to tyrannize and, important to this study, his capacity to arouse sympathy. The latter trait attended Napoleon's sensing of betrayal whenever he had lost the game. The sensing, in turn, encouraged his followers to sanction whatever revenge Napoleon pursued as a compensation.

Two last facts will finish this depiction of the Noble Outlaw. One, the Noble Outlaw is not pathological about harming others. That type of Outlaw is Marlowe's Tamburlaine or *Mein Kampf's* Hitler, and is not heroic. The Noble Outlaw *napoleonienne* sees harm to others as mere necessity in a rude game, with no pleasure in the act for him. Two, the Noble Outlaw is courteous to women. The attribute speaks well for Robin Hood and Karl Moor, medieval specialists in *curteisye,* but speaks badly for our Frenchman.[2] According to Bourrienne, Napoleon had little time for women except for sex, insults, and parlor-diplomacy.[3]

The task remains of how to structure Napoleon into his Noble Outlaw reputation. For this task I shall defer to John H. Matthews' strategy of setting up Napoleon's life into three periods. The first period, 1769 to 1799, will represent Napoleon's rise into prominence, a hero become *nonpareil.* The second period, 1800 to 1815, will include his becoming First Consul and Emperor; then, as Noble Outlaw, an exile and at Waterloo a catastrophe. The third period, 1816 to 1821, will center on Napoleon's banishment to Europe's Elba, then to Africa's Saint Helena. Death in 1821 will have finished the man, but will not have finished his legend. A resume of what-since, therefore, will conclude my depiction.[4]

In the first period, an early characteristic of Napoleon was a fearsome passion. The characteristic made him central in many a childhood situation. Says Napoleon: "I was quarrelsome and combative and afraid of no one. I hit and scratched my companions and they were all frightened of me."[5] Napoleon is referring to his childhood in Corsica where his parents allowed him freedom to develop. In France, however, at the age of nine-and-one-half, he found in his school at Auton rules for everything—stern rules, compelling his conformity. Furthermore, fellow students, *royalistes francaises,* condescended to him and called him "slave," France having conquered Corsica. Napoleon felt abused and undone. Later at Brienne he remarked to his classmate and subsequent biographer Louis-Antoine de Bourrienne: "I will do these French all the mischief I can."[6] A suspicion of being put upon and rejected exists within Napoleon's words. Deep within, he felt unequal, "betrayed," vengeful.

At Napoleon's school in Brienne, 1779-1784, two more outlaw characteristics become prominent. For one, Napoleon illustrated his knack for leadership. In the winter of 1783, for instance, Napoleon organized his fellow-students into opposing armies for attacking and defending positions, and once, after heavy snow, he had the students prepare siege works out of the snow. Then he conducted battles, attacking, defending, hour after hour. His professors were impressed with what they saw.

At Brienne Napoleon revealed also a personal heroism in response to an insult from a student named Pouget des Illets. The student had commented to another that Napoleon's Corsican father was a mere "court-usher" and not a nobleman. Napoleon, enraged—another instance of his passion—challenged Pouget des Illets to a duel. Since both Napoleon and Pouget were only fourteen, the school would not allow the confrontation to develop. Kircheisen reports in *Napoleon's Autobiography* that Napoleon had been determined to effect the duel.

From Brienne Napoleon moved to the Ecole Militaire in 1784, and one may assume in Napoleon's one-year stay an intensification of character traits noticeable at Autun and Brienne. The same may be assumed for Napoleon's stay in Corsica, 1786-1788, while on leave of absence from his regiment. In 1789, however, another characteristic of the Noble Outlaw becomes noticeable, his lack of cruelty— pathology—in dealing with people. In March of that year Napoleon was despatched with troops to Seurre to quell a civil disturbance. There, without firing a shot, he manipulated the mob out of their riot. Napoleon's speech to the mob reveals his composure under stress as well as a knowledge of mob-psychology. "Citizens," said Napoleon, "my orders are to fire on the *canaille;* respectable people may withdraw." The mob did not wish to be identified as "trash," thus dispersed as "citizens."

A major betrayal occurred to Napoleon in a crisis between France and Corsica at the beginning of the French Revolution, 1789. Torn between loyalties, Napoleon decided upon Corsica, already in revolt. Arriving on the island in September, he went to work for Corsican independence. Unfortunately, his actions earned him the hostility of Paoli, a Corsican national hero and the real leader of the Corsican movement. In a struggle for leadership, Paoli won, and Napoleon had to return to France.[7] Napoleon spoke of his countryman's refusal to accept his leadership as a "betrayal." The incident was traumatic in its after-effect on Napoleon.[8]

Next a significant event and, with it, Napoleon's rise to power: the siege of Toulon, 1793. The English had taken advantage of a Royalist insurrection to seize France's Mediterranean port. Thereafter, a General Jean-Francois Carteaux, with Napoleon in command of the artillery, was sent to recapture the city. Carteaux could not effect recapture, and the siege was entrusted to Napoleon. After the shift of command, the troops abandoned Carteaux to the man to storm Toulon for Napoleon.[9] Napoleon recorded in his diary: "Three days after my arrival the army had its artillery organized." This statement may only reflect Napoleon's satisfaction with the efficiency of his artillery, but I suspect that it also reveals not only Napoleon's satisfaction with the outcome of his campaign, but also Napoleon's confidence, now entire, in his leadership.[10]

Napoleon's reward for taking Toulon was a promotion to general and a staff position in Paris. The occasion becomes more eventful when one knows that Napoleon did not want to go to Paris, but once there had, at 25, his first real experience with women. He wrote in 1795: "Women reign supreme; at the theatres, in the streets, in the bookshops. In the libraries of scholars one sees alluring forms. Of all the countries in the world, this is surely the one where women deserve to hold the reins of power." For a while Napoleon wondered if he might not be seized by a "craze for marriage." Military ambition, however, overruled this temptation and the fact, whatever it does to his Noble Outlaw image, remains the characteristic of Napoleon. Bourrienne notes, for instance, that Napoleon "seldom said anything agreeable to females, and he frequently addressed to them the rudest and most extraordinary remarks."[11]

Napoleon's first major military effort was the Italian Campaign, 1795-1797. With the campaign, Napoleon, now 26, was to emerge as a French hero: an undoubted *non pareil* to his army, but perhaps only a Noble Outlaw to his observant staff.[12] Regardless, Napoleon's response to the new challenge was superb. The other generals were resentful at being commanded by one younger than they; nevertheless, Napoleon assumed immediate command. The Duc de Raguse reported: "From the moment when Bonaparte took over, his personality imposed itself upon all. Though somewhat lacking in dignity, and decidedly gauche in attitude and movements, he had something imperious in his glance, his bearing, and manner of speaking; one felt compelled to listen."[13] When his army became stalled at a bridge, Napoleon assumed personal charge. "I went to the front myself," he reported. "I asked the soldiers if they were still the victors of Lodi. My appearance produced such an impression on the men that I decided to attempt the passage once more."[14] Napoleon's need to be the central figure comes out in his remarks to Miot de Melito at Montebello during the campaign. The remarks bring out a Machiavellian thrust in Napoleon, one which a Noble Outlaw might have, but not a *non pareil.* To Miot de Melito:

> What I have done so far is a mere nothing. I am only at the outset of the career in store for me. Do you think my triumphs in Italy are meant to aggrandize the lawyers of the Directory, the Carnots and Barrases? Do you think they are meant to found a republic? What an idea! A republic of thirty million men with our manners, our vices! How should it be possible? It's a chimera the French have run mad for, which will pass like so many others. What they need is glory, and not theories which mean nothing to the French. Let them have baubles, that's all they ask. They will play with them and follow on, always provided one is clever enough to conceal where they are being taken.[15]

Napoleon's next big event was his campaign to annex Egypt, 1798. Talleyrand had gotten Napoleon into Egypt, and Talleyrand returned him to France after hearing that the *Directoire* was about to topple. From Marseilles to Paris, Napoleon was welcomed as France's man of the hour. One must compare the eulogy to him to that of Lindbergh after his flying the Atlantic or to that of John F. Kennedy on his Inauguration Day. Like Kennedy at least, Napoleon received the adulation with an emotion well tempered to put the moment to use. As a hero, he could connive the better with Talleyrand and Sieyes, a member of the *Directoire,* to become supreme over France. At 30, Napoleon was ready to rule.

If Napoleon's career had ended at thirty, he would have to be seen as an authentic *non pareil,* rivalled only by Goethe and Hugo in having achieved the image so young, and rivalled by no one for popularity, including Lord Byron. His achievements seemed magnitudinal, he had been victorious, and furthermore he had won for France. What awaited him then was a legend, and one arrived for him in the form of an epithet. Napoleon became *le petit Caporal.* The epithet is reductive, plain, summative, peasantish, endearing. It put on a pedestal one receiving a national idolatry. Napoleon was to receive no greater term of endearment in his subsequent periods of war and peace.[16]

As one knows, after becoming hero *non pareil* of France, Napoleon became Europe's hope as First Consul, the liberals' curse as Emperor, and Europe's outlaw when his invasion of Russia failed. Whatever his reversal, however, he did not lose his hold on France until Waterloo. Charisma, a common touch, and administrative and military genius played their part in Napoleon's remaining *non pareil.*[17] Nevertheless, a Noble Outlaw lay in embryo within, balancing gain with loss, mixing law with lie, and measuring the times before becoming time's victim. Illustrations from Napoleon's second period will show what I mean.

One. Napoleon's first step upon becoming First Consul in 1799 was to stifle the Senate while praising its independence. The act re-enforces a hero's need for being a central figure. The act is also arbitrary, dangerous to one's *non pareil* imprint. *Two.* The early years of Napoleon's second period were characterized by numerous assassination attempts by the deposed Royalists. Thus, one evening, when it was known that Napoleon was to attend the opera, a carriage with a barrel of explosives inside was left on a street the First Consul's carriage would have to follow. The intention of the assassins was to touch off the explosion just as Napoleon's carriage came up beside the charge, but due to an error in timing, the First Consul's carriage had already passed when the explosion took place. Napoleon continued on to the opera and, upon arrival, gave no indication that anything out of the ordinary had occurred. But the crowd awaiting him had learned what had taken place, and cheered him as he stepped from his coach.

Three. Assassination attempts continued and now Napoleon turned to personal expressions of justice in retaliation. Thus, the Duc d'Enghien, Bourbon prince—and an innocent man—was secretly tried

106

and killed as requital. Napoleon had exclaimed: ''Am I a dog to be simply shot down in the street? Are my murderers some sort of holy beings? . . . Every day there are these attacks on me. It is high time I requited war with war. The chief criminal shall answer for it with his life.'' *Four.* In 1804 Napoleon proclaimed the First Empire with him as emperor. The coronation took place in Notre Dame de Paris on December 2 amid pomp and pageantry not seen since the 18th Century royalty. The climax, as is well known, occurred when Napoleon, taking his coronation crown from the Pope, placed it on his own head. An egoistic act, no doubt, but in a romantic age also the compulsion of one who would not have a rival for center stage.

Five. From 1805 on, wars—wars until Napoleon's defeat in 1815 at Waterloo. During the period, however, Napoleon's control of the French remained undiminished, for every stage of his domination was accentuated by heroism and leadership. At Austerlitz in 1805 Napoleon visited his troops. The effect on them is described by General Thiard.

> Scarcely had we reached the line when Napoleon was recognized, and the men stood up at sight of him. We had hardly gone fifty paces when a bit of wood across our path made him stumble. But luckily we caught hold of him in time and he did not lose balance. Then the grenadiers, of their own accord, took the straw on which they were lying, twisted it up to make something like torches, which they set alight, and then walked in front of us to light (the way for) the general, making the air ring with their shouts. This impulse was electric. All down the line torches were made, and each troop, as it were, took over escort duty from the one before.[18]

Six. The need to dominate, as compulsive to Napoleon as fascinating to the French, comes out in a conversation with his Minister of Propaganda and Police, Joseph Fouche. The time is 1812, just prior to the invasion of Russia. ''My duty is not fulfilled. I mean to finish what is only roughed out. We need a European code, a European court of appeals, the same currency, the same weights and measures, the same laws. I must make all the nations of Europe into the same nation and Paris into the capital of the world. That, my lord, is the one ending that will do for me.''[19]

Napoleon's success at war came to an end with his Russian Expedition. With his retreat from Moscow, the Allies became his pursuers, took Paris on March 31, 1914, and led by the Czar Alexander I of Russia, began the task of what to do about Napoleon. Permanent exile to Elba was to be his sentence. Napoleon's new image as Noble Outlaw had commenced its altering effect upon his national image as *non pareil*.

Napoleon, as one also knows, would not accept Elba—too far from the center of things is a light but relevant reason—and thus sailed from the island on January 25, 1815, to land in France on March 1. Resistance from the Bourbons was immediate. A battalion of troops were detailed to Laffray, close to Cannes, to stop him. Undaunted, Napoleon approached within pistol shot of the Laffray battalion and cried out: "Soldiers of the Fifth Regiment: Do you recognize me?" Kircheisen speaks of the effect upon the Regiment as indescribable. Kircheisen continued:

> Marchand's aide-de-camp kept on shouting, "There he is! Fire!" but no one stirred. The Emperor then took a few steps forward, opened his overcoat and cried: "If there is any soldier among you who wishes to kill his Emperor, he may do so. Here I am!" This was too much for the soldiers, who had already been worked upon by the sight of the vast crowds that accompanied Napoleon. The soldiers threw away their weapons and rushed to *petit Caporal,* swearing to follow him wherever he might lead them [Kircheisen, ed., 689]

Waterloo, 1815, was to bankrupt the image of Napoleon as France's *non pareil* of men. Not only did he lose a battle at Waterloo, but also his hold on the French, who now sensed long wars ahead of them. Thus Napoleon's retreat from Waterloo toward Paris became a prelude to second exile, this time to Saint Helena. Napoleon's seal as Noble Outlaw was now to become set. With six years of life left him, he had become liable to the tag of a hero with a flaw, less visionary than egoist, less avenger than criminal, and less master than militant. These images would filter into Napoleon's resentment and gloom to create a man who had ceased to be Prometheus. Thus, in an age of freedom encouraging the individual to become great, Napoleon had risen but had not held his height. Napoleon's third period, 1816-1821, was about to begin.

The noticeable characteristic Napoleon took with him to Saint Helena was one he had inherited from Waterloo, his feeling of betrayal.[20] Aboard the English warship transporting him there, he had already begun his speech: "The men of 1815 were not the men of 1792. The generals were afraid of everything." On Saint Helena, the sense of betrayal grew to fasten on former friends in France. "Had I continued prosperous, most of them who abandoned me would probably have never suspected their own treachery. In any case, I was more deserted than betrayed; there was more weakness about me than treason. . . ." In 1816, he remarked on his recent defeat: "Ah, unhappy France! . . . [I]n less than a week I three times saw success slip out of my hands! Had it not been for the desertion of a traitor, I would have crushed the enemy at the beginning of the campaign. I would have crushed them at Ligny had my left done its duty. Again, I would have crushed them at Waterloo had my right not failed me." Then, poignantly, it seems to me, in 1817: "My own opinion is that I ought to have died at Waterloo; perhaps a little earlier. Had I died at Moscow, I should have probably had the reputation as the greatest conqueror ever known. But the smiles of Fortune were at an end." As a Noble Outlaw, of course, Napoleon remained miles above his confrere, the Common Man, and had become, if less than Charlemagne and Alexander in victory, nevertheless equal to Hannibal and Rommel in defeat.

I would conclude this chapter by saying that one's impression of Napoleon's character in his first period (1769-1799) is that he had gained awareness of his heroism and leadership but did not know what to do about them. John Matthews describes the period as Napoleon in purest state of being. The condition no doubt assisted Napoleon's rise to *non pareil*. In his second period (1800-1815), Napoleon understood his endowment and put to use the parts that would serve him best. Thus, Napoleon grew in passion, leadership, heroism, and power, and picked up the habit of dispensing personal justice. In this period Napoleon spoke less of betrayals, had less often to punish, and could be magnanimous to the enemy. In combination, each attribute working on the others, Napoleon became a hero of his age and the master of France. Popular and outsize, he emanated "glory" and France adjudged him a demigod. Before him, of course, awaited not Valhalla or Heaven, nor even Prometheus's rock; rather, Saturn's grove transferred to Pandemonium. Elba then was his destination, and removal out of the sun of Europe.

In his third period (1816-1821), as Matthews observes, Napoleon had no need to manipulate followers at Saint Helena and could no longer, after Waterloo, manipulate his followers in France. Thus he had little alternative except to recriminate, absolve and accuse, fume and fuss—in short, express betrayal. It is the response that a Noble Outlaw needs for his wounds. It is Napoleon's characteristic that seems most dismissable to us.

In the Twentieth Century, Napoleon's genius has been celebrated,[21] his campaigns studied, his Napoleonic Code for France assayed, and his dream for Europe understood. Nothing that he accomplished or envisaged, however, has atoned for his slaughter of Europe and remonarchizing of France. That he had stabilized France was offset by his reduction of much of Europe to rubble. That he would envisage a Grand Plan for that most brilliant of continents was offset by a rout of nations, each celebrating its difference of culture and sameness of blood. Not even a *non pareil* could have achieved what he, Noble Outlaw, had flubbed. Napoleon could, then, have been intimating the impossibility of his dream when he expressed his duty to France as her emperor. "The French," he said, "require a prince to be active, enterprising, and courageous, and above all (with a smile) to take them robbing abroad." Any hero might make this remark, but he would require like Napoleon a realism beyond wit to see that whatever he did for La Belle France, that lady must always approve. France did for a while, then made an outlaw of her prince when his "robbing" went awry. Today, by testimony of the best Napoleon scholars since 1850, Napoleon remains engroved in Pandemonium: a super-Saturn, heroic and leaderly, but found out. I doubt that he will be changing residence.[22]

Endnotes

[1] By *non pareil* I mean unequalled, unparalleled; by *manque,* flawed (in character) and abortive (in judgment). Meanings from *The New Cassell's French Dictionary* (Rev. by Denis Girard with the assistance of Gaston DuLong, Oliver Van Oss, and Charles Guinness). New York: Funk and Wagnalls, 1962).

[2] See Peter Thorslev's *The Byronic Hero: Types and Prototypes* (Minneapolis: Univ. of Minnesota Press, 1962) for the standard description of the Noble Outlaw—especially page 68.

As a sophisticated Noble Outlaw, concerned equally with law and order and aggrandizement and war, Napoleon has never become a folk hero. Nor was it possible for him in his time to remain a hero *non pareil* or to become a Byronic hero. The hero *non pareil* is too ideal for Napoleon's long-term image and too little flawed; the Byronic hero is too consciously damned and too much flawed. The Noble Outlaw represents, then, a mean between the other two heroes—it centers Napoleon between Hugo and Goethe, authentic olympians, and Byron and Trelawny, dimensional blights. Said another way, Napoleon is closer to Goethe's Gotz than to Goethe's Werther, is leagues away from Byron's Manfred and Cain, and well removed from Byron's Childe Harold. He is, I shall add, too hearty and mature for Chateaubriand's Rene, too overwhelming for Joyce's Dedalus, and too little diabolical for Bronte's Heathcliffe or Dickens' Steerforth. He is, then, closest of romanticism's hero-types to Schiller's medieval bandit Karl Moor. Karl Moor, I should add, may be the *ur*-type of the Noble Outlaw and, along with Goethe's Werther, of the romantic hero. (The literary types just referred to are to be found in Goethe's *Gotz von Berlichingen* and *Die Leiden des jungen Werthers* and Byron's *Manfred, Cain,* and *Childe Harold's Pilgrimage;* also, in Chateaubriand's *Rene,* Joyce's *Portrait of an Artist as a Young Man* and *Ulysses,* and Dickens' *David Copperfield.* Schiller's characterization of Karl Moor is in *Die Rauber* and Charlotte Bronte's of Heathcliffe in *Wuthering Heights.* In the tradition of the *non pareil,* outlaw, and *manque* heroes—all aspects of the romantic hero—is Thomas Wolfe's Eugene Gant. Gant however seems to me least identifiable with the hero-types mentioned in this study.

[3] Louis Antoine F. de Bourrienne, *The Life of Napoleon Bonaparte,* trans. unlisted (Philadelphia: Carey and Lea, 1832), p. 188. Hereafter cited in the text as *Bourrienne.*

[4] I would acknowledge my debt to John H. Matthews not only for the periods depicting Napoleon's advent into noble outlawry, but also for facts here and there illustrating Napoleon as both hero *non pareil* and noble outlaw. I have not yet located Mr. Matthews for permission to use these facts, but would have the reader know that they seem numerous enough to me to constitute a condition of collaboration with Mr. Matthews.

[5] Friedrich M. Kircheisen, ed., *Napoleon's Autobiography,* tr. Frederic Collins (New York, 1932), p. 7. Hereafter cited in the notes as *Kircheisen.*

[6] Bourienne, p. 35. Jacques Bainville puts the phrase, "I shall do all the harm I can to your Frenchman," thus illustrating how translators can create another condition for pedantry. I should add that Hamish Miles, translator of Bainville's *Napoleon* (Boston: Little, Brown, 1933) is not up in phrasing to the unknown translator of Bourrienne's *Life of Napoleon Bonaparte*.

An addendum. James M. Thompson looks upon Napoleon's defense of Corsica at Brienne as the beginnings of Napoleon's ambition and self-discovery (see Thompson, *Napoleon Bonaparte*, New York: Oxford Univ. Press, 1952, pp. 10-11). I would add that Napoleon's being underdog at Brienne set up the condition for Napoleon's becoming Noble Outlaw when his reversals set in after 1812.

[7] Kircheisen, pp. 27-40. J. Christopher Herold notes in *The Age of Napoleon* (New York: American Heritage, 1963, p. 14) that Napoleon's training in France made Napoleon "French" to the Corsicans, thus ruining his chances of being accepted as a Corsican revolutionary.

[8] Jacques Bainville brings up of the ironic fact that Paoli had been Napoleon's hero at Brienne, hence Napoleon's leaving Corsica to Paoli represented his saying "farewell to Rousseau . . ., to ideology, to the romance of revolution. . . ." Bainville continues: "[Napoleon] believed no longer in the goodness of human nature. . . . Even his style changed to taut and nervous. [Thus] Bonaparte had emerged from the age of sentiment. [His] skin of youthfulness was sloughed" (pp. 32-33). J. C. Herold concurs with Bainville in his depiction of Napoleon's change (see Herold, *Age of Napoleon,* p. 30).

[9] General Carteaux, a former adjutant-general in the republican army, was a painter of military pictures and portraits at the time of being entrusted with the Toulon siege (see James M. Thompson, *Napoleon Bonaparte*, New York: Oxford Univ. Press, 1952, p. 33 for added details on that siege).

[10] See Kircheisen's *Napoleon's Autobiography* for a well-put account of this incident; also, *The Corsican: A Diary of Napoleon's Life in His Own Words,* comp. by R. M. Johnston (Boston: Houghton Mifflin, 1910), p. 11. *The Corsican* is hereafter cited in the notes as *Corsican.*

[11] Bourienne, p. 188. Bourrienne's report on Napoleon's hostility to women has been challenged by R. F. Delderfield, who has said that Napoleon had, in addition to two wives, at least 12 mistresses. Guy Breton adds that Napoleon was obsessed with women,

a fact that Delderfield sustains in observing that Napoleon "at heart lived and died a romantic." (See Delderfield, *Napoleon in Love,* Boston: Little, Brown, 1959, and Breton, *Napoleon and His Ladies,* tr. Frederic Holt, New York, 1966, for accounts contradicting Bourrienne's.) Delderfield and Breton impress me as incurious about bed-warming pranks, whereas Bourrienne impresses as having been in full observation of Napoleon in action. I therefore have included Bourrienne's statement in the text rather than Delderfield's and Breton's.

[12] Napoleon's bravura streak at Ratisbon illustrates his ability to say the right word to the right soldier at the right time. "Soldiers! You have lived up to my expectations; your bravery has more than compensated for your lack of numbers. . . . The enemy, swayed by treacherous rulers, seemed not to have remembered what sort of army you are. You have shown him you are more terrible than ever. . . ." (Charles Parquin, *Military Memoirs,* tr. and ed. by B.T. Jones, Hamden, Conn.: Archon Books, 1969, p. 88). This speech could seem like noble rant to a staff already familiar with Napoleon's promise of cities, provinces, and riches to the same soldiery in the Italian Campaign even while he assured the Italians that he would respect their property. "We shall wage war like generous enemies, for our only quarrel is with the tyrants [the Austrians] who have enslaved you." See Herold, *Age of Napoleon,* p. 59, and Robert B. Holtman, *Napoleonic Propaganda* (Baton Rouge: Louisiana State Univ. Press, 1950) for related instances of doubletalk *napoleonienne.*

[13] Kircheisen, p. 80. The Duc de Raguse is addressing a Noble Outlaw, whether or not conscious of his discrimination. His comment is consistent with the Duc de Raguse's turning over Paris to the Allied forces after Waterloo rather than defending Paris until Napoleon could arrive there. The decision insured Napoleon's second exile from France (Parquin, p. 183).

[14] Kircheisen, *Corsican,* p. 49. Napoleon defeated the Austrians at Lodi and entered Milan five days later. (Herold, *Age of Napoleon,* p. 60).

[15] Jean Savant, ed., *Napoleon in His Times,* tr. Katherine John (New York: Nelson, 1958), p 64. Hereafter cited in the notes as *Savant, ed.* Like Oswald's willful murdering in Wordsworth's *The Borderers,* Napoleon's psychology is all outlaw, one who is "out," but would be "in." His psychology is also nihilistic and surly—that of one who will be "in," then, after an overflow of homage and glory,

and will be "out" again at Saint Helena.

[16] Napoleon may have enjoyed three periods as a *non pareil,* but only one during his lifetime—from the Italian Campaign (1795-1797) to the Russian Expedition (1812). The remaining two periods occur posthumously: one, from 1830 to 1850 in France, when reaction to the 2nd Empire and acclaim of Las Cases' *Memorial* (dictated by Napoleon at Saint Helena) brought eulogy to Napoleon from the poets, reburial in Paris, and canonization, tomb and all, in 1840. Mixed responses from hard-headed historians, to be mentioned later, nullified that *non pareil* image to leave an American homage coinciding with our homage to the Robber Barons from about 1875 to the 1920's, when individualism was rampant and power an elixir from the American Dream. Though accepted everywhere and still honored in France, Napoleon has been no one's *non pareil* hero since the 1930's. See Pieter Geyl, *Napoleon: For and Against* (New Haven: Yale Univ. Press, 1949) for relevant commentary on Napoleon's posthumous reputation.

[17] Robert B. Holtman has observed that Napoleon was only completely effective when addressing lower-class Frenchmen. He could not win over scholars and foreigners because of a failure to understand the individual mind *(Napoleonic Propaganda,* p. 217). I question this observation, but pass it onto the reader as another effort, like mine, to classify Napoleon.

[18] Kircheisen, pp. 256-8. Also, see Savant, ed., pp. 168-169 for related incidents. More heroism occurred at Wagram in 1809. French losses were heavy and many generals killed. Napoleon galloped to the front, shouting, "The whole Artillery of the Guard—forward!" Thereafter, he hurried from point to point to view the battlefield, disregarding the shots falling about him [Kircheisen, ed., p.472].

[19] Savant, p. 270. Holtman mentions Fouche infrequently in *Napoleonic Propaganda.* The fullest study of Fouche's association with Napoleon is Stefan Zweig's *Joseph Fouche: The Portrait of a Politician* (New York: Viking, 1930).

[20] The defeat at Waterloo gave Napoleon a supreme option for exercising his "betrayal and retaliation" theme. Charles Parquin reports that the Waterloo victors had reached Paris before Napoleon; thus, this speech by Napoleon to his troops: "Soldiers! The enemy has stolen a march on us and has taken Paris. We must drive him out. Unworthy Frenchmen, emigres we have pardoned, have flaunted the white cockade and have joined with the enemy. These cowards

will pay the full price for their new treachery! Let us now resolve to vanquish or to die, and to compel all to respect our tricolour cockade which for twenty years has accompanied us on the path to glory.'' Immediately from the soldiers: "Long live the Emperor! To Paris!'' Hope was in everyone's heart, said Parquin (p. 183).

[21] Albert Guerard believes the image of Napoleon as genius, or even as titan and demigod, was conceived in Saint Helena and came of age during the 1830's and 1840's with the return of Napoleon's ashes to France *(Napoleon I,* New York: Knopf, 1967, p. 192). Helping in such an *image epique* was Stendhal's assertion that Napoleon was equal to Caesar *(A Life of Napoleon,* New York: Howard Fertig, 1977, pp. 183-184), Balzac's and Beranger's idealization of Napoleon as a savior and miracle-maker for France, Hugo's commemoration of Napoleon as an idol of the poets, and Musset's verdict that Napoleon was mighty, overwhelming. See Pieter Geyl, *Napoleon: For and Against,* tr. Olive Renier (New Haven: Yale Univ. Press, 1949) for the above facts.

On the other hand, as ballast, Talleyrand, Napoleon's sponsor, saw Napoleon's death as "just an item of news,'' and Chateaubriand, Lamartine, and Vigny sided with the Bourbons and remained aloof from Napoleon even after his hero-worship had begun (Guerard, pp. 190-191). Madame de Stael was indignant over Napoleon, condemning him as anti-religious, anti-traditional, without human sympathy, and egoistic without human sympathy (Geyl, pp. 17-18; 220).

[22] In 1848, Louis Thiers, in a dozen volumes, admired but remained critical of Napoleon (Geyl, p. 55); in 1863, Jules Barni ridiculed Napoleon's moral indifference, pride, and contempt for humanity (Geyl, pp. 75-76); and in 1865, Edgar Quinet described Napoleon as an Italian, victimized by Dante's *De Monarchia* (Geyl, p. 84). In 1890, Hippolyte Taine deplored Napoleon's "Italianate'' quality of scorn, manipulation, and egoism (Geyl, pp. 135-136). Still, Taine's imprint of Napoleon does not influence Frederic Masson's praise of Napoleon in 1894 as being a man of the people and of unequalled greatness (Geyl, p. 208).

Twentieth-century writings on Napoleon have been more balanced in that they have, like Thiers, seen both good and bad in Napoleon, and thus have offered him both homage and disdain. Bainville, for example, has seen Napoleon as simultaneous tyrant and liberator— his reign a waste, but himself a survivor of his age (Bainville, p. 404).

Georges Lefebvre has accredited Napoleon with having the striking mixture of brains, ambition, imagination, and fire, along with an awesome will to power and a belittlement of freedom (Lefebvre, *Napoleon,* pp. 421-449). Albert Guerard has seen Napoleon as a man of greatness obliterated by a yen for propaganda and brazenness (Guerard, p.185). Lefebvre may have best summed up Napoleon, however, as a second Prometheus doomed to die, a human genius struggling with fate, and a man of ambition who has left mere traces of his accomplishment (Lefebvre, 421-449). The paradoxical descriptions delineate Napoleon as a Noble Outlaw, but they could have as easily placed Napoleon as an anti-hero, had Lefebvre been writing in 1965 instead of 1935.

Perhaps J. Christopher Herold has best rendered Napoleon in *The Mind of Napoleon* (New York: Columbia Univ. Press, 1955). The Napoleon-formula, says Herold, is work, tirelessness, concentration, speed, and cynicism; also, practicality, self-interest, a distrust of systems and ideologies, and the belief that man is weak, selfish, and easily guided. To these elements Herold also adds the belief of Napoleon that "the strong are good, the weak are wicked"; that Destiny and Luck are elements in the human calculus; and that planning and willfulness are essential to accomplishment (Herold, *Mind of Napoleon,* pp. xx-xxv). Not all of these attributes and notions coincide with Napoleon's being a Noble Outlaw, nor do they depart from the ironic blend of achievement, failure, and blindness that characterized Karl Moor, Oswald, and, inevitably, Manfred and Cain. Thus the Twentieth-Century critics of Napoleon seem to agree with Goethe that Napoleon had one of his age's greatest minds; where the critics would depart from Goethe would be in their insistence that, unlike Goethe, Napoleon misused his mind.

PART FOUR:

GOTHIC

CHAPTER SEVEN

Toward a Gothic Metaphysics: Parts

To construe the Gothic novel, one must refer to nine Gothic parts. I am aware of the fact that Aristotle required only six to define the parts of tragedy;[1] that Plato required none to specify the dangers of art;[2] that Kant and Coleridge were so wrapped up in describing genius and imagination that neither became proficient in describing literary genre;[3] and that only the Chicago Critics of the twentieth century have supplied the consummate labellings one recognizes as systematic, demonstrable, and, behold, reducible to parts.[4] I have been influenced by those neo-Aristoteleans in my organization of the Gothic novel.[5] Without them I would not have discovered Aristotle; with them I have learned to detect what is Gothic. It is enough to have received from either God or man a coherent order of any art. It is more than enough to have received as well a key to all art, including that rarest trauma and greatest literary spook, the Gothic novel.

The essential parts of the Gothic novel, without which no other parts are effective, are not those Gothic familiars *machinery, trapping,* and *atmosphere,*[6] but *horror, suspense,* and *shock.*[7] Above all, horror. The state represents terror's excess. It is coincident with *supernatural,* another excess, and seals the form of the Gothic novel. I do not exclude terror, horror's mean, from having its Gothic range. Still, horror is where terror is headed when one leaves Ann Radcliffe's *The Romance of the Forest* or *The Mysteries of Udolpho* to pick up Matthew Gregory Lewis's *The Monk* or Charles Robert Maturin's *Melmoth the Wanderer.*[8] In the latter works arise the investive awe and dread fundamental to the Gothic effect. And therein occurs the greater prospect that Gothic horror will be felt. When felt, horror becomes the signification of the genre, just as pity becomes that of tragedy.[9] Not felt, the plot's workings toward horror nevertheless reveal the temper of the genre, and, as important, the changes needed for creating a felt state.

The second Gothic part is *suspense* and the third *shock*.[10] Let me get to the point: Without suspense, no shock; without both suspense and shock, no channeling of Gothic action into Gothic effect. I am suggesting that horror, suspense, and shock are as connected in the Gothic novel as oxygen and breath. Thus, if no shock, then no horror; and, if no horror, then not enough Gothicism, and no Gothic aesthetic of any accuracy or depth.

With the parts entered and signified, however, one can make ready for *machinery, trapping,* and *atmosphere,* and those overlapping addenda, *setting* and *device.* But know these three or five elements to be Gothic topping—needed, spectacular, but unfulfilling when not serving the essential three, of horror, suspense, and shock.

Of fourth magnitude among Gothic parts is *sublimity.*[11] The term is troublesome since general and intellectualized. In the Gothic novel, it can describe human awe before a supernatural act or consternation at a villain's guile. It can express a character's response to nature's best or worst, or a reader's response to a plot's actions or events. It illustrates like melancholy the complexity of human nature; like miracle it can cause trembling and elevation. It takes a blending of suffering, fear, and hopelessness in the plot to achieve melancholy in the reader; it takes joy made immense or mystery become menace in the plot to achieve sublimity in the reader. For joy made immense, ecstasy is the final effect, whether in character or reader; for mystery becomes menace, dread, great dread energized by suspense.

I find sublimity in the Gothic novel operating best as the preliminary to horror. As a preliminary, it represents an apprehension, a perception, recording the shock and suspense in the Gothic novel before its overflow into horror. If felt in this relationship, sublimity becomes awe in the reader—astonishment, an impalpable state-of-being, intimate and intimative. Unfelt by the reader, sublimity remains mere words, dormant, awaiting the character and event that will make it vital.

I suspect that sublimity, however well Ann Radcliffe writes about it[12] and Gothicists work at it, is not often "felt" by the reader.[13] I have experienced one instance of it in *The Mysteries of Udolpho* and one in *The Italian*. I have experienced more, however, in *The Monk, Frankenstein*, and *Melmoth*.[14] The difference is that, in the latter three novels, one encounters both the suspense and shock necessary to an achieved sublimity. Especially the suspense. For if shock will intensify suspense, and hence heighten the sublimity of an event, a progression of too many or too powerful shocks will hasten the horror that dissipates the sublimity of that event.[15]

What we have said on sublimity in the Gothic novel is certainly not the last word on the subject. But it does take one a step beyond Edmund Burke on the subject, and the right step if sublimity is to be charted.

How will the charting go? Always along the reader's way: by tracing his interior shifts from sensings to states to emotion; from curiosity, then, to apprehension to fear; from conditions of choice to conditions of necessity;[16] and from conditions of order and quiet to those of chaos and clamor. But before this charting can begin, sublimity must have been either felt or sensed. By the reader, mind you. Once felt, or sensed, however, its components should form in a line. Otherwise, Aristotle has not defined "felt" tragedy,[17] Burke has not written on true sublimity,[18] and I am not an organic critic.

Suffering is a fifth part in the Gothic novel, with *pity* as its complement. Suffering is a character trait. It occurs in both the innocents who fall and the "Fausts" who are driven.[19] Pity, on the other hand, occurs in the reader who witnesses their actions. The innocents, whether a Theodore, a Matilda, or an Isabella,[20] do not represent dominating Gothic fare, as many a Gothic plot will attest.[21] Rather, the innocents come on as pawns of persecution, as moral display, as alternatives to angry "Fausts," and as signs that, outside, a world exists that is not tossed and awesome, or even overwhelming. Still, the innocent is uncommon in the Gothic novel who is not as pitiful as pitiable.

With the Faust-types—with Melmoth, Ambrosio, and Manfred, for instance[22]—the suffering is central to the plot, and the pity for the type, when present, is summarizing and catalytic. When it occurs in the Gothic plot, it will have brought the plot at that point to a head, and set up a tone and direction that must be either implemented or countered. The "Fausts," then, sustain the importance of suffering and pity in a Gothic plot. They also project, by contrast, how bland is innocence to the reader advanced in experience beyond devotion to a Teddy Bear or an heirloom doll.

Sixth part, another mood, more complex than suffering, and with less determinable effect. I speak of *despair,* a state-of-being word with an evoked melancholy as its defining complement. A state of the blahs characterizes both despair and melancholy, but felt blahs only in melancholy, and then only in a vital Gothic plot. *Caligula, Cat on a Hot Tin Roof,* and *No Exit* evoke their share of the blahs;[23] the response however is only incipient in Marlowe's retinue of deadly sins in *Doctor Faustus.*[24] The state is standard in the Gothic novel, not only for the character in despair, but also, in an outsurge of horror, for the overcome reader. As *despair,* the state characterizes both the bleakness of innocents under duress and of hero-villain subject to moral reckoning. As *melancholy,* it characterizes the reader's satiation with bestiality, gore, and injustice.

In the Gothic plot, an aesthetic pleasure is endemic in despair and melancholy, but always in the limitation that the condition is less definable, and thus less pleasurable, than that of suffering and pity. In *Dejection: An Ode,* Coleridge describes melancholy as tenacious;[25] Shakespearean critics are aware of it in the problem plays;[26] psychologists account it as the vale of no hope. With hopelessness at hand in the Gothic novel, one should expect to encounter despair among the characters and melancholy in the reader. Yet, as we have said, melancholy, or the blahs, has its aesthetic office.

With horror and suspense, and sublimity and shock, and with suffering and pity, and despair and melancholy, one has included what seem to me the elements making that genre viable. Without them, one has to conclude, there is no Gothicism. With them, one has to acknowledge a unique genre, related to tragedy and romance, and with an ancestry beginning perhaps with Euripides.[27]

Still, if become generic, the Gothic novel has not been enclosed. To effect that enclosure, one must refer to the three last Gothic parts: the Gothic *spectacle,* the Gothic *characterization,* and what I call the Gothic *excess.* Thus, seventh, Gothic spectacle.

Or should the seventh be, instead, *characterization?* I shall hazard the thought that characterization should precede spectacle in all novels except the Gothic. In that genre, Gothic spectacle is the obstacle which Gothic characterization does not surmount. One could argue, indeed, that Gothic characterization, in its limitation, has forced the enhancement of Gothic spectacle to save the novel.

What about Gothic *spectacle?* It is a matrix out of which comes much Gothic action, is an affair of the senses, and may be, in any Gothic plot, as diverse as the wind in the arras, the castle on the cliff, the ghost in the abbey, or, best of all, the torture in the tower. Spectacle in the Gothic scene is an intimate of suspense, an element in sublimity, and a setting for characters engaged in suspenseful action or at moral odds. But spectacle, though it may generate a mood, will not, alone, generate an emotion.

I am saying, then, that Gothic spectacle is limited to its immediacy as display. If it becomes symbolic, like Manfred's medieval pile Otranto,[28] it has transcended *spectacle* to take on *meaning.* If it becomes humanized, it has achieved *characterization.* One "sees" spectacle most; one "hears" it more than one "feels" or "smells" it. I am still searching for the English Gothic spectacle that, Thyestes-like, one has "tasted." An ideal spectacle will include at least three senses at work for complexity and depth of presentation.[29] I account as good spectacle the nudged object in a dank dungeon that, by lantern and nose, becomes a decomposing corpse. A better spectacle is Baudelaire's rotting woman, overrun by larvae and flies, being guarded by a hungry dog.[30]

Within Gothic spectacle can be located much of the so-called Gothic *machinery,* some of the Gothic *action,* all of the Gothic *setting* and *atmosphere,* and many of the Gothic *properties* and *trappings.* One must always differentiate Gothic spectacle, however, from Gothic thought, meaning, or characterization. If it becomes any of these, it has ceased to be Gothic spectacle.

Eighth, *characterization.* The Gothic character, whether good or evil, or neurotic or normal, comes first into being as supernatural or natural. As supernatural, its many forms include ghosts, specters, vampires, monsters, witches, and devil's advocates. They include a Bleeding Nun, a Wandering Jew, symbolic Fausts, and humanized Lucifers. Werewolves and genies belong among these supernaturals, and male and female ghosts. This listing represents typically no more than a parade of agents, with enough to do but not enough substance to come alive.

In natural form, the Gothic character includes bandits, hermits, hero-villains, and noble brigands; mysterious females, demonic heroes, and decaying corpses. To these one must add maidens in flight, nuns and monks in crises, prisoners in dungeons, and assassins at large; and, not least, various levels of lords and ladies, princes and kings, and German, Spanish, and Italian counts. With their human dimension, these characters have a pulse-beat that the supernaturals lack, but their relevance to the plot can be as dimensionless and circumspect.

A dilemma of natural characters in the Gothic novel is that they frequently exist in both natural and supernatural worlds without power to decide between them.[31] This plight one can accept if their situation is probable to the Gothic plot. But the dilemma goes under the eye when one discovers that, like Melmoth, they possess demonic power they can't shake; or, like Ambrosio, a monk's appetite for God, Satan, and sex; or, like Vathek, an aristocrat's mania for high fun, low ridicule, and absurd punishment and pain. Nor is the dilemma lightened by those innocents, the young heroes and heroines.[32] Though granted no access to the supernatural kingdom, they show great powers of survival and, without stint, conspicuous valor. Furthermore, in suffering they are meek and, when events go awry, modest and patient. Thus, two groups, the possessed and the pure, emerge in the Gothic plot; they are types commissioned to be people, but ending up as breathing abstracts of goodness and evil, purity and flaw, and nobility and depravity.

I am conscious among these Gothic naturals—and supernaturals—of too many creatures of excess, of the imagination turned loose, and of actions gone limitless. Thus, they irradiate beyond rather than meld into a probable plot. They cancel out realities to enact prodigies. They over-achieve to create not an archetypal reality but an unreality, when what was needed was a believable reality, whether supernatural or natural. I account the Gothic characterization as the ill-conceived element in the Gothic novel.

Ninth, *excess*. Without excess in the Gothic novel, there would be a typicality and concreteness of plot that one could even call romantic realism. With excess arrives those nutrients of the nerves: imbalance, abnormality, and escape into fantasy. Some excesses in the Gothic novel are:

1. Excess in dimension: size, solidity, height, and depth.
2. Excess of states: hate, love, greed, sin, and pride.
3. Excess of flaw—found in the grotesques: the hunchback, villain, and lunatic; and the witch and demon.
4. Excess of reality: supernaturalness, hallucination, and nightmare.

5. Excess of sex: rape, vampirism, wantonness, lust, and, in *Vathek,* homosexuality.
6. Excess of effect: shock instead of recognition, tears instead of restraint; and murder instead of natural death. Then, sublimity instead of sense, throbs instead of intimations, and screams instead of articulation. Not least, blasts instead of breeze, hallucination instead of dream, and shouts instead of hallos. I shall not add, but should, horror instead of terror: preferably.[33]

The strength of excess as an aesthetic term is its accurate description of frantic Gothic activity. The weakness is its lack of organic lodging in the Gothic plot. One can talk about characters, describe actions, narrate episodes, and pinpoint climaxes without once mentioning *excess.* Still, the term must remain as both description and sometime indictment of the Gothic novel. Excess, then, is the necessary orphan: belonging, but not "in"; at hand when needed, but out of pocket when not. Of all the Gothic parts it is the most investive and present; yet, of all the parts, it is least isolable as a function. Take or leave *excess* as a Gothic part. I take it in knowledge of its presence.

If these are the Gothic parts in the Gothic novel for "Toward a Gothic Metaphysics," now must follow, to finish up, differentiations on horror and terror, postscripts on supernatural, spectacle, and sublimity, and the functions of the Gothic novel. With these, the author will be finished as well. Expect to find him thereafter on some Carpathian height, fighting werewolves and bats; shining relics and cross at cannibal plants; or, leaping crevice and moat to get at the castle that houses the maid who will wed the boy that is locked below by a madman just transformed into *The Unbelievable Thing.*

Endnotes

[1] See Aristotle, *De Poetica.* Trans. Ingram Bywater; in *The Basic Works of Aristotle.* Edited by Richard McKeon (New York: Random House, 1941), pp. 1460-1461. To Aristotle the six parts of tragedy are plot, character, diction, thought, spectacle, and melody.
[2] See Plato, "Phaedrus," *Dialogues.* Trans. Benjamin Jowett (New York: Random House, 1937), I, 249; also, "Ion," I, 289; and "Apology," I, 405.

³ For Kant on genius, see *Critique of Aesthetic Judgment.* Trans. James Creed Meredith. Great Books of the Western World (Chicago, 1955), XLII, 525-526; for Coleridge on the imagination, see *Biographia Literaria.* Edited by J. Shawcross (London, 1954), I, 59, 153; II, 14-17, 268. Coleridge's transferral of evidences of the imagination from the poet to the work of art is sensitive and revelatory, but vague for explication purposes.

⁴ See *Critics and Criticism* (Edited by Ronald S. Crane. Chicago: Univ. of Chicago Press, 1952) for representative inclusions of the Chicago Critics. I cite particularly in this volume Richard McKeon's "The Philosophic Bases of Art and Criticism," pp. 463-545; Ronald Crane's "The Critical Monism of Cleanth Brooks," pp. 83-107; Elder Olson's "A Symbolic Reading of the *Ancient Mariner,*" pp. 138-144.

⁵ However much my debt to the Chicago Critics for this paper, I could not omit the refining influences of Eliseo Vivas, Allen Tate, William Empson, and Cleanth Brooks. They have made me over the years textually aware and criticism-conscious. In this paper their influence is peripheral but not nebulous. For like the Chicago Critics, they represent the kind of thinking one assimilates—sometimes with acknowledgment—into one's own thinking.

⁶ *Machinery, trapping, atmosphere.* Elements frequently used to describe the Gothic process. See Montague Summers, *The Romantic Quest* (New York: Russell and Russell, 1964); Devendra P. Varma, *The Gothic Flame* (New York: Russell and Russell, 1957), and Eino Railo, *The Haunted Castle* (London: G. Routledge and Son, 1927) for a conventional use of these Gothic trademarks.

⁷ *Horror, suspense,* and *shock.* Eino Railo has written on Gothic suspense in *The Haunted Castle* (1927), pp. 319-327; Devendra Varma, on horror (as distinguished from terror) in *The Gothic Flame* (1957), pp. 129-132. No one has singled out shock for what seems to me a necessary addition to the Gothic vocabulary. *Shock* represents the impactive extreme of *surprise.* It is to horror what surprise is to terror—the implementation producing horror rather than terror as Gothic effect.

⁸ *The Romance of the Forest,* etc. The first of many references to the English Gothic novel in this paper. They will constitute the primary evidence.

⁹ *Signification.* Used instead of *soul* to eliminate comparison with Aristotle's ascription of *plot* as the soul of tragedy. But, *horror*

is at the soul of the Gothic plot. It could be no place else.

[10] *Shock.* As suggested, *surprise* is not enough. *Surprise* means "to take unawares," "to come on suddenly." *Shock* is more impactive; it is even concussive. See *Webster's New World Dictionary* (Englewood Cliffs, N.J.: Prentice Hall, 1972), pp. 1315, 1433, for the distinctions.

[11] *Sublimity.* For standard writings on *sublimity* see Longinus, *On the Sublime.* Trans. G.M.A. Grube (Indianapolis: Bobbs-Merrill, 1957); Edmund Burke, *A Philosophical Enquiry into the Origin of Our Ideas of the Sublime and the Beautiful* (1756). Related to Burke, and written within the decades of the English Gothic novel, are Kant's commentary on Beauty and Sublimity (1790)—for a reduction of the commentary, see the *Syntopicon. Great Books of the Western World* (Chicago, 1955), I, 115-116; Coleridge, on sublimity (see *Coleridge's Miscellaneous Criticism.* Ed. Thomas Middleton Raysor. Cambridge: Harvard Univ. Press, 1956, esp. p. 148); "Some Remarks on the Use of the Preternatural in Works of Fiction," *Blackwood's Magazine,* 111 (1818), 648-650; "On the Supernatural in Poetry by the Late Mrs. Radcliffe," *New Monthly Magazine,* 16, pt. 2 (1826), 145-152; and Nathan Drake, "On Gothic Superstition" and "On Objects of Terror" (see Drake, *Literary Hours.* 3 vols. London: Longmans, 1820, I, 105-114; 269-275). The standard scholarly text on sublimity is Samuel Monk's *The Sublime: A Study of Critical Theories in 18th-Century England* (1935).

[12] Ann Radcliffe's statements on sublimity occur in "On the Supernatural in Poetry by the Late Mrs. Radcliffe" (1826). Her efforts at creating the effect in her novels are legion.

[13] This subjective statement raises the question of how fluently one can speak for another's reading of a work. I believe that the plot guides us each and all into related responses to a work. But the degree of response thereafter can vary in the individual. How broad is that margin of variation remains, of course, the indeterminable.

[14] *The Italian* by Ann Radcliffe. Generally accepted as her next best "Gothick" to *Udolpho,* but possibly more attuned than *Udolpho* to Gothic sublimity.

[15] I dislike literary axioms, for they cannot encompass or control a subject as axioms of algebra and geometry can. These three, however, are appropriate for summarizing Gothic sublimity. *One.* To be vivid, Gothic sublimity must be accompanied by suspense and shock. *Two.* Gothic sublimity, as said, operates best as the preliminary

of Gothic horror. *Three.* To Gothic sublimity must be added, always, its potential for becoming Gothic horror. I would have you see Gothic sublimity as the thrill that predicts the scream that congeals the reader into transfixion.

[16] *Conditions of choice.* Options, then, remaining from which to choose. Coleridge uses *volition* in this sense. *Conditions of necessity.* No options remaining; rather, an inevitable sequence of causes and effects proceeding to a natural conclusion. The notion is Shelley's, taken from Godwin. (See *Shelley's Prose.* Ed. David Lee Clark [Albuquerque: Univ. of New Mexico Press, 1954], pp. 109-112, for a larger discussion.)

[17] Aristotle's "felt" tragedy must center upon how acutely pity and fear have registered in the reader as tragic effects. In Sophocles' *Oedipus Rex,* pity and fear are strong and, up to the end, balanced. In Euripides' *Medea,* fear dominates pity to provide a macabre (Gothic) conclusion. In Shakespeare's *Hamlet,* the tragic effects are muted and reduced by a dispersed plot until after Hamlet's killing of Polonius, and Laertes' expose at the "mousetrap" play. Thereafter, there is much pity and fear, with pity dominating, as it should, at the end.

[18] Burke's treatise on sublimity remains a *chef-d'oeuvre.* Its difficulty in the present is not its lack of cogence, but the fact that *sublimity* has lost its aesthetic purpose for the grimmer set, the realists and the expressionists.

[19] If the "Fausts" suffer, they also rage about to the distractions of the innocents. At the end, like the legendary Faust, the "Fausts" have suffered more than they raged, hence are more pitied than hated.

[20] *Theodore, Isabella, Matilda,* in order, two innocents and a purity. In Horace Walpole's *The Castle of Otranto* (1764).

[21] Elizabeth McAndrew suggests that the innocents may belong in the novel of sensibility beside which the Gothic novel represents a darkened way. See McAndrew, *The Gothic Tradition in Fiction* (New York: Columbia Univ. Press, 1979).

[22] Melmoth: Maturin's suffering protagonist in *Melmoth the Wanderer* (1820); Ambrosio: M.G. Lewis's hero-villain in *The Monk* (1796); Manfred: Walpole's raging tyrant in *The Castle of Otranto* (1764). See Robert D. Hume, "Exuberant Gloom, Existential Agony, and Heroic Despair: Three Varieties of Negative Romanticism," *The Gothic Imagination: Essays in Dark Romanticism* (Pullman: Washington State Univ. Press, 1974) for incisive appreciation of the

Gothic "Faustians."

[23] *Caligula* (1943) by Albert Camus; in *Caligula and Three Other Plays.* Trans. Stuart Gilbert (New York: Knopf, 1958); *Cat on a Hot Tin Roof* (1955) by Tennessee Williams (New York: New Directions Press, 1955); *No Exit (Huis Clos)* (c. 1946) by Jean-Paul Sartre. Trans. Stuart Gilbert (New York: Knopf, 1948). Each a registrant of the Theatre of the Absurd and of the bleakest of modern philosophies, existentialism.

[24] See Marlowe, *Doctor Faustus* (1952), Scene 6.

[25] See Coleridge, *Dejection: An Ode,* St. 2; 11. 1-4.

[26] See David Kaula, "Critical Perspectives," *The Moral Vision of Shakespeare's Troilus and Cressida* (Ann Arbor, 1955) for representative responses to one of Shakespeare's problem plays. Other relevant studies: E.M.W. Tillyard, *Shakespeare's Problem Plays* (London, 1950) and *Shakespeare, Troilus and Cressida: A Casebook.* Ed. Priscilla Martin (London: Macmillan, 1976).

[27] Euripides wrote tragedies, not horror plays. Yet such a play as *Medea* teems with Gothic nuances. Consider Medea's rage and suffering at being abandoned by Jason; her device for destroying Jason's new bride; her killing of Jason's and her children; and, at end of play, her departure in a chariot drawn by dragons. See Euripides, *Medea.* Trans. Woodhull (New York: E.P. Dutton, n.d.). Everyman's Library.

[28] See Elizabeth McAndrew, *The Gothic Tradition in Fiction,* pp. 9-20, for an impressive rendering of Otranto castle. In the instance, Gothic setting has become symbol.

[29] I draw my clue from Laurence Perrine's elegant rendering of the senses at work in the imagery of Browning's "Meeting at Night." See Perrine, *Sound and Sense* (New York: Harcourt, 1963), pp. 45-47. Second Edition.

[30] See Baudelaire, *Une Charogne* ("The Carcase"). A competent translation is by F. P. Sturm.

[31] My position is similar to Tsvetan Todorov's in *The Fantastic.* Trans. Richard Howard (Cleveland: Case Western Reserve University Press, 1973). Todorov's discussion of fantasy is meaningful for the Gothic novel.

[32] "Innocents" is my classification. If there is a standard description, it must be that used by Eino Railo in *The Haunted Castle*: "young heroes and heroines."

[33] The excesses abstracted and enumerated have been noted here and there in the English Gothic novels. The idea of a table of enumerations comes from Montague Summers' listing of Gothic characteristics in *The Gothic Quest* (London: Fontane Press, 1938), p. 35. Summers is distinguishing there ''the Gothic romance'' from ''the novel.''

CHAPTER EIGHT

Toward a Gothic Metaphysics: Postscripts

1. Gothic Terror and Gothic Horror

In *The Haunted Castle*, Eino Railo equates terror and horror as the same emotion, and he is right in that horror represents intensified terror. Still, the equation of terror and horror leads him into an unanalyzed connection of *The Mysteries of Udolpho* and *The Castle of Otranto* with *The Monk* and *Melmoth the Wanderer*. One needs only to read these two sets of Gothic novels to realize that their effect upon the reader varies considerably—enough to compel a critic to examine in detail what happens in Gothicks evoking terror and in those evoking horror. That is the intention of this second chapter on terror and horror,[1] which describes Devendra G. Varma's comparisons of terror and horror; Eino Railo's conditions for arousing terror; and my introduction of elements that attend the arousal of both terror and horror and effect their independence of each other as Gothic responses.

As a result of the analysis I hope to show why horror rather than terror is the definitive Gothic effect, and, considering all parts, the ultimate Gothicism.

First, to Devendra Varma. In *The Gothic Flame*, his prescription is explicit: terror is one element in the Gothic novel, horror is another. Thus terror satisfies the gentle emotions, horror the ". . . violent and tragic passions" (Varma, p. 129).[2] He adds: Ann Radcliffe is the progenitor of terror in the Gothic novel; M.G. Lewis and C.R. Maturin are the progenitors of horror (129). Sardonic villainy and "tearful Amandas" characterize a Gothic novel of terror; diabolical laughter and "vindictive Matildas," the Gothic novel of horror. In the former one undergoes an "awful apprehension"; in the latter, a "sickening realization." In the former one receives a smell of death; in the latter one stumbles upon a corpse (129-130).

Obscurity and darkness are necessary to both types of Gothic plots with a resultant "psychic dread," says Devendra Varma, quoting Alan McKillop (130). In the Gothic novel of terror, however, he adds, one experiences a shudder at the other world, while in the Gothic novel of horror, one experiences gloom and despair before events horrible and revolting. Says Varma: The resultant "psychic dread" is indefinable in the Gothic novel of terror; in the Gothic novel of horror, it becomes a "cutaneous contact with the supernatural" (130).

Again, Varma: Suspense is implicit in the Gothic novel of terror, for, prolonged enough, suspense from vague and uncertain actions and events will excite terror in the reader. On the other hand, when the cause of the terror is known, the reader is propelled into a state of horror. As Varma puts it, an awesome union of "strength, violence, pain, and terror has performed its attack on the mind" (130).

Devendra Varma cites E.M.G. Tompkins' observation that, of the two types of novels, beauty is more apt to be found in the terror novel. Beauty refines terror, Tompkins says, and prevents it from verging on disgust. In the horror Gothic, adds Varma, the writer overturns this union of beauty and terror to convert a romance into a "mere maquillage for horror" (131).[3] Thus, to seal a comparison, out of the turnstiles of the Gothic novel of terror emerge *The Mysteries of Udolpho, The Sicilian Romance, Romance in the Forest, The Old English Baron,* and *The Castle of Otranto.*[4] To be sure, one finds here a plenitude of ambiguity, suspense, and spectacle, but little enough of themes with depth or moment, and, excepting *The Castle of Otranto,* not any theme that does not explain away its supernatural base. By comparison with the horror Gothicks, the characters are muted, the events probable, and the ambiguities crystallized. Says Varma: Look in vain then for motivations toward horror such as black magic, lust, and unpardonable sins; or persons in pursuit of the *elixir vitae* and persons in contact with the Devil. More, expect not laboratories of monsters, tales of skull-headed ladies; and, not least, the dead arising from graves to feed upon the blood of the innocent and beautiful (131). You will find such goings-on, he adds, in Beckford's *Vathek,* Godwin's *St. Leon* and *Caleb Williams,* Lewis's

The Monk, Mary Shelley's *Frankenstein,* and Maturin's *Melmoth the Wanderer* (130).

If Devendra Varma has enunciated differences of terror and horror as Gothic effect, Eino Railo has defined conditions for achieving the effect. Railo centers upon the one evocation—terror—yet, what he says applies to horror as well. I cite you many of his conditions, for they are essential to the Gothic plot and helpful toward a final Gothic appraisal.

Terror, says Railo, is achieved in two ways: by suspense generated from dangers threatening chief characters, and by a de-emphasis of literal flights and battles to introduce "suggestions"— hints, half-sentences, and weird phenomena. These ways excite a "reader's curiosity to the highest pitch," says Railo, and assist him to supply the interpretation most terrifying to him. More, the author tries to take the reader out of his world of realities into one that neutralizes his disbelief and does not question his sanity (Railo 319-321).

On the minus side of the Gothicks, Railo believes that *The Castle of Otranto* does not arouse "terror";[5] that *The Old English Baron* is too lucid to be suggestive (321-322); and that Mrs. Radcliffe's works, though richly suggestive, are too well-explained to evoke terror. On the plus side, however, Beckford's *Vathek* does evoke terror, says Railo, as do Lewis's *The Monk* and Maturin's *Melmoth;* for, unlike Mrs. Radcliffe's works, they contain no "common sense explanations" that permit "the brain to regain control and destroy the effect of the work" (322-323). Thus, Lewis and Maturin, unlike Walpole, Smith, and Radcliffe, bring off a "true terror"[6] in their works; the supernatural and the unnatural events take over the plot, and a haunted castle, demons and ghosts, incest, and a never-ending life tease the reader out of his ordinary way and logic (323-324).

Adds Railo: Terror, also, is to be had through use of the supernatural—for instance, by dealing with supernatural events without argument or explanation, by attaching to supernatural events a "scientific" explanation; and by dealing with horrors reaching into abnormality. One does not achieve terror, Railo concludes, by dealing with supernatural phenomena that can be explained (323-324).

So far, so good. But, I must add, Railo ignores the fact that terror and horror are divergent, and that terror will intensify into horror when well-crafted luridities are not quite explained. *Horror,* though frequently his subject, has not been Railo's Gothic usage in *The Haunted Castle*.

Gothic terror and Gothic horror are, as said, the defining evocations in the Gothic plot, but that pronouncement does not alleviate the enigma of their presence. Like all emotions, they seem to be depthless, possessing layer on layer of relationships and avenue on avenue of meaning. Devendra Varma has projected this possibility in his terror/horror inductions, for he has gone from emotion to characteristic to character to novel, and even to metaphor, in getting at the two states. He could have gone on to twice the number of comparisons and all to one's benefit. But he would not have dispelled the enigma of what elements attend the build-up of Gothic terror and horror themselves. This build-up I would explore. More, I would suggest the limits of terror and horror, for, despite their being impalpable, they are finite and must have limits. Especially would I see terror and horror in a systematic relationship to each other. I shall not argue that such a concentration will afford, as it does, intimations of a universal condition governing not only the Gothic novel, but also our day-to-day terror/horror world. I shall only say that the concentration should confirm two facts: that horror, not terror, is the ultimate Gothic effect, and, when all's said, the ultimate Gothicism. I get to my duties.

I have said in Chapter Seven that the Gothic novel of terror presents fear in its "mean" state. The proof is evident when one adds that pity—pity for the fallen Gothic victims—is pronounced in a condition of "felt" Gothic terror. Pity, indeed, is the underpinning that accentuates the Gothic terror. On the other hand, pity for the Gothic victims is diminished in Gothic horror, and this because of a hopelessness of circumstance in the plot—a hopelessness that has turned fear into horror. Gothic terror, on the other hand, remains clustered with hope—hope for change to a better state—until a state of terror has become at the end irrevocable. Without exception, save in the least crafted Gothicks, pity and hope participate or would participate in every expression of terror or horror.

Another differentiation.[7] Gothic terror, as both Varma and Railo have noted, leans on normal and natural elements and events to surround one's supernatural fears and dissipate them. Gothic horror, I would add, leans on supernatural and abnormal elements and events to expand felt terror into felt horror. This distinction is standard, and the most obvious of terror/horror differentiations.

134

A third differentiation. Railo has noted that Gothic terror relies on suspense to reach a felt state. Allow me to add that Gothic horror relies less on suspense than on shock.[8] One could account for this difference by a simple numerical checkup of the two states of the Gothic novel. The difference goes deeper, however, when one notes the relationship of Gothic terror and of Gothic horror to another state each shares: Gothic sublimity.

Assuming, for instance, the participation of Gothic sublimity in equal degree in both Gothic terror and Gothic horror effects, one may expect to experience Gothic terror—of less shock and more suspense, and of more pity and hope—for a longer duration. By comparison, one may expect to experience Gothic horror—of more shock and less suspense, and of less pity and less hope—for a shorter duration.

Described another way, Gothic terror is investive when felt, and permeating when prolonged. A credibility has been sustained. By comparison, Gothic horror is astonishing when felt, but repulsive and demoralizing when prolonged. Violence, bad sex, decomposition, and demonic villainy combine to rule out hope of change, pity for victims, and resistance to events. Thus, enter the "horrors," the jolts, and, if prolonged, the reader's nausea. The nausea experienced, of course, is not an intended effect. It signals, rather, the reader's rejection of an incredible excess. On the other hand, his "horrors" and jolts reveal a reader wallowing in Gothic bliss.

Another differentiation. Gothic terror, in permitting more pity, comes closer to tragedy in remaining closer to naturals in a natural state. Gothic horror, if tragic, is also spectral and obliterative. Its union of human and non-human elements dissipates its capacity for human tragedy to enforce its sway as a spectacle of shocks. This difference can, but does not have to, condemn Gothic horror as a lighter pleasure than Gothic terror. Still, if so, let it be, for the Gothic novel is not prone toward depth except in the hands of a Dostoevsky or a Kafka. One reads Gothic novels as one views Gothic cinema, for luridities and kicks. The genre is not privy to elucidating, like *Oedipus* or *Lear,* the tragedy of life. It is, rather, an elucidation of events that lean toward tragedy before achieving its state of horror or of terror. Of the two states, I prefer the Gothic jolt to the Gothic tingle, even though the jolt is as improbable as dragons performing rituals of death, and the tingle as personal as children engaged in altarwork at Black Masses. I am conditioned to the unreality of Gothicism. Its unreality is, to me, one of its attractions.

135

Last, and least, Gothic terror and Gothic horror partake of the imagination, an obvious Coleridgean point. But Gothic terror's locus in the imagination is constituted in humanized castles and deeds, even though humanized with a difference. Gothic horror's locus, on the other hand, is constituted in never-never expanses of cliff and sea and ever-ever presences of demon and damned.[9] Thus, on the horror side, Frankenstein's monster, homicidal and depressed, on a polar icepack. On the terror side, Isabella of *Otranto,* upset but intact in an Italian dungeon.

Toward which, then, should the reader gravitate? If the reader is a Gothic buff, I believe that he will gravitate toward Gothic horror, ever more blotted out by fresh whiffs of blood and corpse. If the reader is less Gothic buff than literary eclectic, he may gravitate toward Gothic terror, ever more intrigued by what follows from shadows on the heath and winds in the belfry. I must admit to my predilection for Gothic horror. Short of its overflow into reader's nausea, I find it to fulfill more, transform better, and demand more of the reader. It carries the Gothic novel as far as it can go as Gothic effect; it enlists a more rampant imagination; and it provides the better escape from the everyday world into which one is locked by tragedy and satire. The more I am assaulted by an action inducing Gothic horror, the more I feel exploited. I wanted to be exploited and I have been. Indeed, my frustration is kindled by anything less. Thus, Gothic horror has become for me the most pleasant of Gothic experiences. In such acceptance, then, I reach out toward this collage of facts. Gothic horror, not Gothic terror, is the necessary Gothic effect. It is the gut-growl to which Gothic terror is the polite rumble. Without Gothic horror, expect to receive less Gothicism. With it, expect to receive that beyond which remains no further Gothic horizon. You will have received the ultimate Gothicism.

For every differentiation I have made between Gothic terror and Gothic horror one can find without great search a divergence or a contradiction in some Gothic work. I nevertheless hold on to the differentiations I have made, for they have introduced norms for capturing the Gothic effect. Either emotion, in its deterministic way, calls on certain conditions for its fulfillment, and the conditions of Gothic terror are not those of Gothic horror. One must accept this difference if one is to understand either emotion as a Gothic element, or—I would abuse your brain with one more repetition—the primacy of Gothic horror.

2. Gothic Spectacle

Recognitions. In *The Popular Novel in England 1700-1900,* J.M.S. Tompkins treats prisons, convents, castles, and monasteries as "Gothic setting." Professor Tompkins is saying, I believe, that the Gothic spectacle has become atmospheric. Professor Tompkins also says that the Gothic setting often outweighs the characters they house in Radcliffian "Gothic" (Tompkins 248-264). The impression is accurate and sometimes inevitable in the Gothic plot. For, as stated in "Parts," when characters become types and morality is stripped, and meaning is lessened and action predictable, one's interest in a Gothic plot must center on, say, the anguished scream and the charnel bone. Both scream and bone illustrate spectacle as surely as do raging torrents and crumbled towers.

From spectacle, thereafter, can follow suspense and shock, and those irrationals tone, mood, and effect. Amid such activity, expect the spectacle to become emphatic: symbolic if stressed, and mythic if entered upon a living theme. Expect also one last step, the surest and the best: Gothic spectacle become reader's pleasure.

Gothic Spectacles of Time and Space. Inevitably they show up within those Kantian domains, time and space (Kant 25-28). Gothic spectacles in time, less numerous than those in space, are intimate to the Gothic action and, if well-structured, can enhance the meaning of the Gothic plot. But these spectacles become difficult to manage when interrupted between one action to the next. Horace Walpole and Mrs. Radcliffe, thanks to their way with suggestion and suspense, can pull off this kind of nimble plotwork. Clara Smith and the lesser Gothicists fall victim to the device. Their spectacles, renewed, become mere recurrences, lost in their repetition.

Gothic spectacle in time easier to manage is that located in a consecutive action—thus, a delayed dying, an expanding landscape, an investive storm, or an uninterrupted pursuit. I cite you four instances from among dozens: Ambrosio in *The Monk,* lofted by a demon to a height, then released to fall, mangled and dying, on a river-bank (Lewis 419-420); the detailed exoticisms of Eblis—some symbolic, most not—at the end of *Vathek* (Beckford 153-169); Victor's polar search for his creature in *Frankenstein* (M. Shelley 20-21);[1] and Mrs. Radcliffe's long paragraphs on *nature pittoresque* in *The Mysteries of Udolpho* (Radcliffe I, 42-43; II, 83-84).

The more numerous spectacles in space are visual, and vital or comatose depending upon the resourcefulness of the author. To Montague Summers and Maurice Levy, the castle is the most prominent Gothic spectacle and the most used. Historically the castle is medieval; architecturally it is Gothic. Attempting to capture the atmosphere of that time, the castle becomes a setting for religious ritual, baronial violence, and maniacal pursuits. Let such be. The castle will remain visual—shaped rock, a spectacle in space—unless, like Otranto Castle, it has become a symbolic ruin.

A related Gothic spectacle in space is the ruined abbey. No surprise to me that the abbey remains merely visual unless it becomes meaningful. Once meaningful, however, it can connote an assemblage of themes. It can represent a union of nature and art, the triumph of nature over art, the crisis of nature and civilization at odds, or, in a Wordsworthian sense, as Paul Yvon has noted, a medieval semblance of the past (Yvon 104). In such classifications, the ruined abbey has ceased to be Gothic spectacle in space. It can revert, nevertheless, if taken over by parading ghosts, Sunday worshippers, a Rylstone doe, or a band of bagpiping Highlanders.

3. Gothic Supernatural

Behold the agent supreme in the Gothic novel for improbable and impossible happenings. In *The Fantastic,* Tzvetan Todorov explains that *fantasy*—to him the word is close in meaning to *supernatural*—works on two levels. One level is social, enabling one to cross inaccessible frontiers like sex and death; to escape censorship by making taboos the work of the devil; to make drugs and madness viable; to discuss psychoses otherwise forbidden; and to provide an acceptable layman's brand of psychoanalysis (Todorov 160-161). The other level is literary, enabling one to illustrate an idea through allegory; to keep the action suspenseful; to provide continuity and resolution to plot; and to permit a break from the rules of what is and what is not. Todorov finds that *The Arabian Nights,* Kafka's *Metamorphoses,* and Gogol's "The Nose" illustrate the literary process of the supernatural (162-167). I find the social workings of the supernatural to enter the English Gothic novel especially through *Vathek, The Monk,* and *Melmoth the Wanderer.*

To these activities of fantasy, and of the Gothic plot, I would add that Gothic supernaturalism exists midway between Gothic spectacle and Gothic character, and brings spectacle into characterization to assist the evocation of Gothic terror and horror. In the Gothic novel of terror, the supernatural performs as relief and setting for the human characters; in the Gothic novel of horror, it is major in the Gothic action. Without the supernatural, both kinds of Gothic novel could revert to being tragedy or become that specialty of tragi-comedy, romance. They could not be "Gothic," not even Gothic romance.

4. Gothic Functions[1]

The English Gothic novel has four functions, but one may prefer to add a fifth one. The Gothic novel must *please.* This fact above all other facts. Without pleasing, its other functions will have lost appeal. But the Gothic novel will please if it arouses terror or horror. Indeed, a felt terror or horror represents the ultimate Gothic pleasure.

The Gothic novel should also *instruct,* even as today's Gothicized mocies instruct—*E.T., Star Wars,* and *The Empire Strikes Back.* Always, however, its importance as instruction will be measured, and limited, by its capacity to evoke terror or horror. Incapable of evoking either, its instruction will be slight, and inconsiderable when compared with the Gothic novel's function to please. That a Gothic novel can instruct, however, finds witness in *Frankenstein* and *The Italian.* That it may only please finds witness in *The Castle of Otranto* and *Vathek.* But that it can instruct to the point of a third function—*to persuade*—finds striking evidence in *Melmoth the Wanderer* and *The Monk.* Which would you have? A knockdown on the perils of immortality on earth, or a breakdown on the wages of deception and lust? Either work can move one to a decision. Each one can evoke terror or horror. Although not a characteristic of all Gothic novels, the Gothicks that persuade deepen one's pleasure in a Gothic work.

Fourth, the Gothic novel can *depress*. It can induce melancholy, then, or send one into "dark, dark Gothic." The condition is borderline-bad; the tone, blah-ish; and the response, displeasing. But such can happen in the Gothic novel become horrifying beyond assimilation or boring beyond belief. To me, the Gothick that bores is an aesthetic misadventure; but the Gothick that over-horrifies is one carried beyond plausibility. One should remember that *Measure for Measure* has become important as Shakespearean autobiography in compensation for its dejection and cynicism. The Gothic "dark" novel, with less meaning and plot, and more mischief at midnight, runs closer to the demise that *Measure for Measure* misses. I exclude *The Monk, Frankenstein, The Italian,* and *Melmoth the Wanderer,* successful dark Gothicks, from the mal-imaginings improvised in the gazebos and the boudoirs of England and France, 1785-1850. Today, the latter group are best noted as entries in Montague Summers' *Gothic Bibliography.*

I have omitted a fifth function that, to me, the Gothic novel misses—the creation of beauty, whether through language, idea, or structure. Perhaps I have denigrated the language of *Otranto* and *Vathek* in effecting this exclusion.

5. Sublimity: Epic, Tragic, and Gothic

I submit that sublimity, as literary effect, occurs best and most memorably in three contexts: epic, tragic, and Gothic.[1] Of the three, tragic sublimity is at center, supplying dimension and depth to the adjacent epic and Gothic contexts. Tragic sublimity, indeed, is the essential sublimity, beside which either epic or Gothic sublimity appears as less intense expression. Of the three sublimities, epic sublimity is closer to tragic than to Gothic, and tragic closer to epic. I shall compare epic and tragic sublimity to illustrate that fact. But I shall not be long in introducing the other sublimity of this segment, Gothic.[2]

Tragic sublimity, at whatever height and however felt, will be governed by one's fear of events in the tragedy and modified by one's pity for the sufferers of the events. In this context, hope is strong in the reader and suspense is even rabid. From beginning to end, the effect of tragic sublimity is prominent and, more than any other literary sublimity, is apt to be awesome.[3]

One reason for such awe in tragic sublimity is that the events and characters motivating the sublimity are probable. Another is that the action is closely knit. A third is the fear of crisis and pity for character that compel one as in no other genre. Thus, there occurs a cycle, over and over, in the tragic plot: with fear heightened, sublimity intensifies; with fear yielded to pity, sublimity dissipates. *Oedipus Rex, Antigone,* and *King Lear,* with reversals of fortune affecting the major characters from beginning to end, are crowded with such sublimity-effects. This is another way of saying that *Oedipus, Antigone,* and *Lear* evoke great fear before evoking great pity.

In epic sublimity, fear is enhanced by a condition found in tragedy: nobility of character. Thus, a noble Hector dies after a long chase by Achilles *(Il.* XXII, 11. 90-365); a noble Aeneas endures the loss of his wife *(Aen.* II, pp. 51-53), shipwreck (I, pp. 4-6), and combat (XII, pp. 328-335) to found Rome; and a moral Dante goes through Hell and Purgatory before reaching Paradise *(Div. Com.* I, II, III).[4] Without exception, hope is high that these good epic figures will survive their crises. This hope is perfect preliminary to the sublimity that will accompany the fear of the crisis. Indeed, just as hope is an auspice of the sublimity to follow, sublimity is an auspice of the crisis to be feared.

In the epic, characters and events determine whatever develops in epic sublimity. As in tragic sublimity, the events that arouse fear should be probable, and the characters for whom one is fearful should be human. Alas, then, for the fact that, in the epic, such may not be the case. Especially in the classical epic there are gods of questionable origin, whose eye is omniscient and whose power is omnipotent. The omni-presence and omni-influence of gods of questionable origin cannot help but blunt the arousal of awe in the reader. Thus the effort of a noble Hector to escape a death decreed by Zeus and prosecuted by Athena loses a share of its sublimity. A reader can regret or ignore, but cannot face down, a divine certainty.

Still, the gods can assist sublimity into epic awesomeness if, though a threat to the epic hero, they do not become his catastrophe. At the same time, the epic hero can enhance that awesomeness by remaining noble before godly peril. An incipient aura of sublimity hangs about a reconstituted Odysseus in his battle with the wooers

(Odys. 331-340).[5] A full aura surrounds Aeneas as he survives traps and trials in the Mediterranean only to find more and worse ones in Italy.[6] At no point at the end of the *Iliad* is Hector free of his destined death. Yet, at the end, his nobility is so apparent that sublimity is an inevitable epic result. Nor has it hurt that the Greeks have been proven to be tricky, disorderly, and vengeful.

In Gothic sublimity, the situation alters. Horror becomes the controlling effect—horror aggravated by hopelessness of circumstance. Shock becomes more insistent than suspense in the plot, and horror over the events dissipates much of the pity for the characters under stress. Nevertheless, characters may evoke a fearsome sublimity by their shocking actions. Gothic actions in plays include Phaedra destroying her sons, Iago provoking Othello, and Richard III reigning as state malignity. These acts arouse a Gothic sublimity. In the Gothic novel, there are Melmoth's Faustian sell-out to gain mortal eternity, and Ambrosio's monkish dalliance with Satan and sex.

Gothic sublimity, then, just as epic and tragic sublimity, is the product of characters under dire and sustained stress. But, Gothic sublimity is also a sensing aroused by Gothic convention and device: it is aroused by ghosts that stroll, vampires that prowl, and gibbets that bleed; or by portraits that moan, madmen that prowl, and werewolves that pounce.

Except possibly to Jane Austen's Catherine Morland,[7] this atmospheric sublimity lacks the tension and power of character-sublimity, and this fact, so evident in the Gothic novel, helps to explain why Gothic sublimity is less effective, hence less pleasurable, than either epic or tragic sublimity. The most pleasurable? Tragic sublimity, because it is the best integrated and the most felt. By comparison, epic sublimity is too bound to godly dealings and too often interrupted by lengthy narration. Still, compared to 'Gothic sublimity, epic sublimity retains a more humanized reference, and, if the *Iliad* and the *Aeneid* are worthy examples, offers a greater pleasure to the reader.

I have mentioned that epic and Gothic sublimity derive power from tragic sublimity, and that epic sublimity resides too much within godly decree. On the other hand, Gothic sublimity, in comparison with epic and tragic, resides too much within a dark and divided, and a malign and supernatural, world. It is a world real yet unreal; wanted yet rejected; and fascinating yet repulsive. It engenders quite another response from that engendered by epic and tragic sublimity, and constitutes another reason why Gothic sublimity, more ominous than solid, falls before epic and tragic sublimity in power and pleasure. I have omitted why satire and comedy are lacking in sublimity, and why sublimity is essentially an effect of tragedy. I shall merely say, in concluding, that epic, tragic, and Gothic sublimity are not only the best and most memorable of literary sublimities, but also constitute the foundation of all other instances of literary sublimity, whatever the genre and whether felt or not.

Endnotes

1. *Gothic Terror and Gothic Horror*

[1] The first part on Gothic terror and horror is to be found in Chapter Seven of this book.

[2] Borrowed by Devendra Varma from Ernest Bernbaum. Professor Varma's first distinction may not represent an auspicious separation of terror from horror as Gothic effect. Still, it presents enough to indicate the difference of a novel by Mrs. Radcliffe from one by M.G. Lewis. Mrs. Radcliffe's terror "satisfies the gentle emotions" because it represents a gentle terror at work upon the reader. M. G. Lewis's horror, on the other hand, is constituted of elements violent enough to shake up both gentle and hardy reader. I should add that Professor Varma's division of effects operates best within the Gothic genre. His division will not carry over, for instance, into tragedy, whether Greek, Renaissance, or modern. I offer Euripides, Webster, and Tennessee Williams as evidence of this fact.

[3] *Maquillage*. French for "rouging" or "bepainting." *Maquillage* suggests a mere imitation of the real Gothicism, which has a stronger action and effect.

[4] If the list represents my examples of terror Gothicks, to follow are Varma's of horror Gothicks. As said, the contrast between the two types of Gothics is substantial.

[5] Railo does not believe that *The Castle of Otranto* achieves an arousal of terror; Varma believes that the novel does achieve it. I would side with Varma to the extent that the conditions surrounding *The Castle of Otranto*—its characterizations, actions, and events—

indicate that there will only be terror aroused, if any emotion. In the Gothic novel of terror, the suspense outweighs the shock, the supernatural is balanced by the natural, and the characters rarely exceed their probability. In the instance, terror is the most that one can expect as a final effect. Still, one may not even receive that effect unless one is rested and ready for a jaunt to some never-never Bessarabian tower via an awesome Danube winding slowly through Carpathian heights and some dread bandit's rivertrap.

[6] "True terror" is Railo's expression for "felt" terror, the aesthetic description commonly used in 20th-century criticism.

[7] I have shifted from comparisons of Gothic terror and Gothic horror to differentiations between them. The difference is small but meaningful. Comparisons are what is done in inductive listings such as Varma's. Differentiations, a more subtle form of analysis, are what must occur in formal criticism. Here, all parts of the subject are considered in working relationship to each other.

[8] To be sure, the reader will experience shock in a Gothic novel of terror, and suspense in a Gothic novel of horror; but the supply of suspense in the former will over-ride the presence of shock, and the supply of shock in the latter will over-ride the presence of suspense.

[9] *Cliffs, seas, spectral domains:* aspects in Gothic context of the romantic Infinite *(Infinito),* if one may go by usage of the Infinite by Leopardi, Coleridge, Blake, and Ibsen.

WORKS CITED IN THIS SECTION:

Railo, Eino. *The Haunted Castle.* London, 1928. All parenthetical references are to this edition.

Varma, Devendra G. *The Gothic Flame.* London: Arthur Barker, 1957. All parenthetical references are to this edition.

2. *Gothic Spectacle*

[1] Mary Shelley's spectacles are brief but sharp, and well-integrated to the action and the characterization underway. The spectacle referred to here is but one of many in *Frankenstein,* and not more effective than the others.

WORKS CITED IN THIS SECTION:

Beckford, William. *Vathek*. New Trans. by Herbert B. Grimsditch. London: Nonesuch Press, 1929.

Kant, Immanuel. "Spectacles of Space and Time," *An Immanuel Kant Reader*. Ed. and Trans. with Commentary by Raymond B. Blakney. New York: Harper, 1960.

Radcliffe, Ann. *The Mysteries of Udolpho*. London: J. M. Dent, 1931. 2 vols. Everyman's Library.

Shelley, Mary (Godwin). *Frankenstein;* or, *The Modern Prometheus*. Berkeley: Univ. of California Press, 1984.

Tompkins, J.M.S. *The Popular Novel in England 1700-1800*. London: Constable, 1932.

Yvon, Paul. *"Le Sentiment du 'Gothique' et son Interpretation chez William Wordsworth," Le Gothique et la Renaissance Gothique en Angleterre (1750-1880)*. Caen: Jouan et Bigot, 1931.

3. *Gothic Supernatural*

WORK CITED IN THIS SECTION:

Todorov, Tzvetan. *The Fantastic*. Trans. Richard Howard. Cleveland: Case Western Reserve Univ. Press, 1973.

4. *Gothic Functions*

[1] My winnowing down of Gothic literary functions to four has occurred after reading the following critical works:

> *To Please*
> Aristotle's *Poetics;* Horace's *Art of Poetry;* Coleridge's *Biographia Literaria;* and Wordsworth's *Preface to the Lyrical Ballads (1800)*

> *To Instruct*
> Horace's *Art of Poetry;* Sidney's *An Apology for Poetry;* and Pope's *Essay on Criticism*

To Persuade
Aristotle's *Rhetoric*

To Depress
No defined critical source here other than those picked up from reading existential writings such as Camus' *Caligula,* Sartre's *No Exit,* and Tennessee Williams' *Cat on a Hot Tin Roof;* also, earlier expressionistic writings such as Eliot's *Prufrock* and *The Wasteland,* Joyce's *Ulysses,* and Kafka's *The Castle* and *The Trial.*

I should add in behalf of these functions that they represent under-pinnings below which no critic has gone in explaining the Gothic novel. By comparison, Todorov's social and literary functions represent intermediate values, especially important to our thinking about the Gothic novel, but not necessarily of continuing value to another generation in another century. On the other hand, the function *to please,* for instance, is a constant, beset to be sure by variations on what is pleasurable in succeeding generations, but never losing its autonomy as the phrase that sums up the variations. One must bow low before such permanence.

5. *Sublimity: Epic, Tragic, and Gothic*

[1] Necessarily literary sublimity is our subject although one could include related sublimities in game-plots, dream-plots, and life-plots, each of course of the most perilous and lively sort. What is not included in literary sublimity, except under unusual conditions, are sublime forms of architecture—plazas, skyscrapers, and Gold Coast mansions—and sublime vistas of nature such as the Grand Canyon at dawn or a quiet sea at dusk. These visuals have size, dimension, beauty, splendor, and power. They leave imprints of grandeur, and they incite in the viewer the beginnings of awe. They do not in themselves, however, invite the terror that attends a strongly felt sublimity.

Viewing the Empire State Building at long range, for instance, will excite nothing of sublimity in the viewer. Seen at short range, it will evoke an awe before its massiveness and height. Viewed from the top, looking down, it can excite an awe coupled with fear to an intense degree. The problem there is how the viewer is to survive a grandeur that besets one with dizziness and weakness, and makes one feel small and abject.

What occurs to the viewer atop the Empire State Building can occur to one at the Grand Canyon upon experiencing its depth and height and shapes and colorations; or at sea, when the sea has advanced from a calm to a storm, or from schools of dolphins to port to swarms of sea-snakes to starboard.

I am saying then that sublimity is not a rare subject. It is even possible to achieve the state with Mary Poppins and Mickey Mouse. One's real problem with sublimity is how to isolate it from the suspense that induces and the fear that dissipates its awe.

[2] I shall not be long in getting into Gothic sublimity, since what I discuss here is little more than an exploration, a preliminary to a project at least book-length in its demand upon the scholar. I shall be satisfied merely to have presented the possibility of that book-length study.

[3] Wordsworth's "It is a beauteous evening, calm and free" and Milton's "Lycidas" express a sublime experience on the part of each of the poets, but do not effect an awe within the reader. Gray's *Elegy,* Shelley's "West Wind," Keats's "Grecian Urn," and Tennyson's *In Memoriam* reflect ranging states of sublimity in their elevation of theme. Nevertheless, they do not evoke the awe consonant with felt sublimity. I am saying, then, that lyric forms, the ode, elegy, and sonnet, in their brevity and narration, cannot project a felt sublimity. On the other hand, the dramatic monologue can. For a test, read Browning's "A Grammarian's Funeral" and "Andrea del Sarto"; or Eliot's confessional *Ash-Wednesday;* or Hopkins' *The Wreck of the Deutschland,* and possibly Yeats's *Among School Children.*

[4] I invite the reader to consider these sublimity norms in reading *The Divine Comedy.* In the Hell sequence, sublimity will derive from the fusion of awe with fear; in the Purgatory sequence, from the fusion of awe with suspense; and in the Paradise sequence, from its own transcendence, without infraction of fear or suspense. *The Divine Comedy,* better than any work I know, reflects the range of sublimity in literary form. *The Divine Comedy* is also the work most subject to losing that range to a reader not ready to put together a dense and complex plot. One can pick up the import of the *Iliad* and the *Odyssey* in a first reading. One can pick up the import of *The Divine Comedy* in a first reading only if well advised in advance of the work's structure and content. Otherwise, one will have to wait for, say, a third reading,

or, better, a lifetime of experience and insight to appreciate the epic's sublimity.

⁵ In his assault upon the wooers of Penelope at the end of the *Odyssey,* Odysseus is aided only by Telemachus, Eumaeus, and Eurycleia among mortals. More numerous, the wooers represent great odds against Odysseus, enough to invoke suspense over how Odysseus can possibly defeat them, then awe from the vengefulness with which he maps out his slaughtering. The reader of course already knows that Odysseus will manage the wooers. The gods have ordained that outcome. Thus blunted is the reader's response to the sublimity implicit to that event.

⁶ The burning of Troy, a Mediterranean storm, the Dido passionale, and the intrepidities of Venus and Juno may be more dramatically posed, and more often read, but they present no competition in magnitude of danger or of achievement to Aeneas's combat with Turnus or the Trojan's battle with the Rutulians for Alba Longa.

⁷ See Catherine Morland's response to phenomena in her bedroom for a prime example of human overwhelment before Gothic device *(North. Abbey* 166-171).

WORKS CITED IN THIS SECTION:

Austen, Jane. *Northanger Abbey. The Novels of Jane Austen.* Collated by R.W. Chapman. London: Oxford Univ. Press, 1923. Vol. V.

Dante Alighieri. *The Divine Comedy.* Trans. Jefferson Butler Fletcher. New York: Macmillan, 1931.

Homer. *Iliad.* Trans. with Introd. by Richmond Lattimore. Chicago: Univ. of Chicago Press, 1951.

_____. *Odyssey.* Trans. by S. H. Butcher and A. Lang. Introd. by John A. Scott. New York: Macmillan, 1930.

Vergil. *Aeneid.* Trans. with Introd. by Kevin Guinagh. New York: Rinehart, 1955. Rinehart Edition.

CHAPTER NINE

Maurice Levy's *"Structures Profondes"* in the Gothic Novel

The intention of Maurice Levy in "Structures Profondes" is to introduce ideas—*"les bases profondes"*—underlying the surface detail of the English Gothic novel. Readers already into my miscellany of the English Gothic novel (Salzburg, 1986-7) will have encountered numerous ideas in existential, Marxist, and surrealist commentaries on the Gothic Novel (see Hume, Sypher, Matthews, and Varma in I: Contexts), in symbolic and Freudian interpretations of *Otranto* (see MacAndrew and Kallick in II: Texts), and in Jungian concepts in the Charles Brockden Brown critique (see Fiedler in IV: Coll. Goth. 2).

Professor Levy's "Structures Profondes" is in obvious good company with these Gothic studies; it is gratifying to add that these studies are in even better company. "Structures Profondes," more than any other study I know, has effected a major analysis of Gothicism. In depth, Professor Levy's study belongs with Professor Varnado's exploration of Gothic terror as a "numinous" expression; in breadth and concentration, Professor Levy's study simply has no equal.[1]

Professor Levy has adopted two approaches for determining the "structures profondes" of the English Gothic novel. One he describes as *"l'axe horizontal et sociologique,"* which treats social and political origins of the genre; the other, as *"l'axe vertical d'histoire,"* involving no *"histoire"* as conventional history, but much *roman* as *conte* (another meaning is *histoire)*[2] for illustrating the genre's psycho-mythic origins. In *"l'axe horizontal,"* Professor Levy is objective and causal, with journals, letters, and events held in hand for explaining the novel's beginning. In *"l'axe vertical,"* he is subjective and analogous, with Freud, Jung, Piranesi, and Gothic landscape and architecture held at hand for interpreting the Gothic plot. Thus, one receives from the first approach a controlled topic operating within social and historical bounds; from the second, an excursion among Gothic symbols and signs for conceptualizing the Gothic plot as *"reve,"* dream. I shall not judge on which of the *"axes"* Professor Levy's reputation depends. I shall say that he has seen with right the necessity of both for getting at the genre. The result is a Coleridgean show, with the conceptualist in Levy overshadowing the historian. That's good enough when one considers that the same could be said about Paul Hazard, Paul Oskar Kristeller, and Walter Jackson Bate.

Professor Levy's rationale for the social and political origins of the English Gothic novel hinges on whether the genre has stemmed from the French Revolution of 1789 or from the English Revolution of 1688. Supporters of the French Revolution have claimed, says Levy, that the novel represents an evocation of the anguish and violence of the time, a class warfare, *"les reves sauvages"* of troubled minds, a symbolic destruction of political tyranny, or a Hegelian imbalance between what is and should be, whether material, social, or cultural. Professor Levy's sources for these explanations range from de Sade (1800) to Sadleir and Breton (1927 and 1937) to Serge Jutin (1962).

Levy does not find these explanations cogent. Once out of France and into England, he finds for instance little mention of the French Revolution in the Gothic novel, or, if mentioned, without importance for the Gothic plot. He finds also the English woman-Gothicist declaring for English law and state, and protesting woman as natally unfit for politics. Professor Levy adds that Ann Radcliffe and Peter Peregrine, when using France as a setting, turned to the Ancien Regime; that Radcliffe was conservative in temper, Maturin toryish in politics, and both social conformists in their writings. Finally, says Levy, citing Georg Lukacs, England in the 1790's was in a post-revolutionary period of its own rather than in France's revolutionary one. Thus, Levy can say: "Si le roman 'gothique' est habite par l'esprit d'une revolution, c'est d'abord de celle de 1688 qu'il s'agit." He adds: "La Revolution de 1688 avait ete religieuse autant que politique: en meme temps qu'elle abolissait les derniers vestiges du despotisme seigneurial, elle consacrait le rejet definitif du catholicisme et confirmait par dela tous les extremismes, l'esprit meme de la Reforme."[3]

Three other factors, independent of the French Revolution, brought the English Gothic novel into existence. According to Professor Levy, these were (1) the Enlightenment, (2) England's turn toward natural law after Newton and Locke, and (3) her profound shift thereafter in national mentality.[4] Professor Levy points out that skepticism toward the supernatural and the marvelous engendered by the Enlightenment permitted religion's substitute, the myth, to take hold in the middle class; and the loss of religious faith permitted the growth of a world of Gothic action and events. Thus, instead of believed mysteries, inducing a fear of the hereafter—of the *"Au-dela,"* as Professor Levy puts it—one had as substitute an aesthetic shudder, Gothic in nature and effected by, not God, but by literary man.

Professor Levy continues: After England discovered Locke and Newton, it passed from *"l'age magique"* to *"l'age scientifique"* and from *"l'age de la poesie a celui du roman."*[5] Thus, nature and natural law rather than religion and the imagination became masters of the English mind, and the poetry of Shakespeare, Spenser, and Milton yielded to the realistic novel of Richardson and Fielding, After the realistic novel, however, England recreated a literary *"age magique"* in turning to the Gothic novel. This change took the English novel out of *realite* into *reve,* with *reve-personnages* performing *reve-faits*[6] in a Gothic setting.

The English Gothic novel as *"reve"* is Professor Levy's way of advancing "Structures Profondes" out of a causal hook-up of background people, ideas, and events into the novel—into, then, a dream-world, says Levy, quoting F. Pages, of "apparitions tenebreuses, . . . scenes nocturnes, creations funeraires, enfantees souvent par un cerveau en delire et qu'on pourroit assimiler aux reves incoherents de la nuit.'"[7] Psychoanalysis, myth, nature, architecture, and art will be Professor Levy's resources for explaining these phenomena. The results will be a manifest on the Gothic novel as an expression of *"l'axe vertical,"* of, then, hidden signs and portents of a collective neurosis, a disturbed sensibility, and even of deep conflicts in the English psyche. The result is a Levyesque world of meanings that transcend English relevance to become continental document.

Beginning with Freud, Professor Levy defines the castle, abbey, dungeon, and tomb in the English Gothic novel as Freudian signs of *"angoisse,"* distress, suggesting ancestral fears. Scenes of violence represent to him hostility images; and father and son conflicts over the mother, sexuality. Then, the French Revolution becomes a romanticist revolt against a classicist father.

Freud's mother-symbols are everywhere in the English Gothic novel, according to Professor Levy. As house-forms, they are represented in the castle, abbey, dungeon, and grotto. One's return to these domains will be effecting a *retour a la mere*.[8] Furthermore, the gate to the castle entered by the returning hero will be feminine; and the hero on knees and hands in the Gothic plot will symbolically be inside the maternal body. Finally, the heroine's faintings, a common occurrence in the English Gothic novel, will represent her regression to a prenatal state.

Professor Levy is not finished with Freud's symbolic woman. The landscape in the Gothic novel represents Mother Earth; the sea is another mother; and a ship at sea, in distress, can be seen as the times in distress, but delivered from the mother-yoke of classicism. But a ship at sea also can represent man's eternal conquest of the mother-sea, Levy adds, and, if the earth and sea are maternal, then also the sky—particularly the moon at night. Last, but not least, the hero's entry into the castle and his descent into the dread dungeon represent his stubborn quest of the mother.[9]

Professor Levy points out that, unlike the mother image, the father image in the Gothic novel is bad. He shows up as *Le Pere Mauvais*—the bad father—the Wandering Jew, the hero-villain, and the Inquisition Fathers. The father has terrible eyes; he uses them to castrate the young hero, as son, I judge, in search of his mother. But the father is also the victim of his son. Incest with the mother figures in the murder of the father by the son; and the usurpation of the father by the son is symbolically sexual.[10] Thus, Levy's Freud in the English Gothic novel.

The symbols of Jung, less individual than Freud's, inhabit man's "collective unconscious," says Levy, and represent a condensation of millions of years and authentic universal meanings. The symbols are, then, archetypes—organs of the collective psyche, *"vertical"* rather than *"horizontale"* in movement, and illustrative of *"le style perpendiculaire."* In this context, a Gothic dwelling illustrates human levels of being, proceeding from the soul's high pitch of "bright consciousness" down into "the (soul's) most archaic beds of being." Thus, at psychological as well as aesthetic work, *"le style perpendiculaire."*[11] The cave or dungeon part of the house is irrational, says Professor Levy, citing Gaston Bachelard. Thus, if one "speaks" of a specter in the hall, one "encounters" it in the cave; or, if not there, then in ruins which, crumbled, were vertical when intact. In the depths of the cave, one is removed from the sun. Here, one tortures and kills, invokes *"le demon,"* and practices necromancy and sorcery. To descend from the sun into the cave is to leave reason and descend into irrationality. Once out of the cave and above, however, the ambulant encounters both daily life and reasonable act. Such a world provides him with an incentive to explain his fantastic experience. Thus, *"au niveau de la conscience claire,"*[12] he dictates an account of the mysteries in the cave. This dictation can become, I shall add, a Gothic novel by Ann Radcliffe or Clara Reeve; or, one step along, an attempt to capture man's *"ciel interieur,"* his surreal interior estate defined by Andre Breton.

Going from cave *(caveau)* to dream *(reve)*, Professor Levy says that the dream of a ghost may be at the same time a dream of the underground, a deep cavern, a half-opened sepulchral vault, or a pit. This surreal transference finds its parallel in a form of dreaming, the reverie. According to Professor Levy, reverie can represent an excavation—a hollowing out—of the mind. Within that confine, one leaves his surface consciousness to go up or down within himself. To descend is serious, Levy adds, quoting Victor Hugo, because the Self deep down *(Le Moi profond)* is shadowy, mysterious, a stranger to itself. One becomes less and less individualized as he goes down, risking not only loss of himself but also the ability to remount to his surface-consciousness. Thus, trapped underground, one is left to wander in a labyrinth of extinguished lamps and narrowing paths.[13] The experience, a familiar one in the Gothic novel, reflects an ancestral anguish of the author, says Levy. But it projects as well the Jungian archetype of the labyrinth, *"l'image fundamental de la prison dynamique."*[14]

This account of man's unconscious depths, simplified as it is, brings one to that exemplar of the archetypal prison, Piranesi. Professor Levy notes that Piranesi's archetypal engravings are imaginary *(Prisons oniriques)*, with space rising and expanding, and making man feel vulnerable and fearful. He adds: The feeling is parallel to that experienced by those trapped in the Gothic labyrinth. Continuing: The prison layout (with its vertical lines and spiraling staircase) is duplicated in the castles and priories of Radcliffe, Lewis, and Maturin. More of a surprise, but nevertheless a challenge, *le roman "gothique"* in development has, says Levy, the structure of

Piranesi's prison.

Thus, on to Levy's conclusion on Piranesi's "Gothic" prison:

> Disons. . . que le Chateau d'Udolphe, l'Abbaye de Sainte-Claire, et les prisons de l'Inquisitions sont, autant que les Carceri d'Invenzione, le lieu mysterieux de cheminements inextricables, le lieu d'interminables descentes, sur des degres chancelants, faites du pas feutre et angoisse des reves, le long de la spirale du Moi. On y decele la meme demarche inquiete qui creuse toujours plus avant les noires perspectives et l'opaque consistence des espaces oniriques, on y retrouve l'univers claustrophobique des grandes profondeurs, ou le reve altere l'espace, l'etire et l'amplifie pour le projeter a la fin, dans la chambre noire du cerveau, "en de fantasmatiques architectures."

> Let us say. . . that the Castle of Udolpho, the Abbey of St. Claire, and the prisons of the Inquisitions are, as much as Piranesi's fictive prisons (*Carceri d'Invenzione*), the mysterious place of fixed approaches, of interminable descents on tottering stairs made of padded step and the anguish of dreams, (and extending) the length of the Self's spiral. One reveals there the same disturbed walk which hollows out always more deeply the dark perspectives and opacities of dream spaces; one rediscovers there the cooped-up world of great depths, where the dream alters the space, stretches and enlarges it in order to design it at last, in the brain's dark chamber, "into fantasmic architectures."

The *"pittoresque"* landscape is a dream-landscape put on paper by the Gothic heroine.[15] Adds Professor Levy: It must be seen as "vertical" in the Gothic novel. Visually, one finds in the *"pittoresque"* landscape a Gothic fortress perched on inaccessible rocks and looking more like *"une vision aerienne qu'a une demeure humaine."*[16] The abbey and the woods of the landscape are vertically in line, and grottoes and caverns—hollowings in the scene—find "vertical" root in Mother Earth. Mountains, an obvious vertical touch, are intended, Levy adds, to invoke fear and dizziness.

As "vertical," but less visual, are Professor Levy's reckonings on The Fall *(La Chute)* in the Gothic novel. It is terrible, irreversible, and, to the dreamer-ambulant, an abyss of evil and damnation. Hell represents one's terminal descent in The Fall, and, as Ambrosio's fall illustrates, it becomes not only the descent of *Le Moi,* but also the collapse of one's moral conscience. Thus, a fundamental difference of *Udolpho* and *Monk* comes to light. At the end of *Udolpho,* the characters emerge from their "dream" to regain their conscious life. In *Monk*—and in *Melmoth*—the dreamer has gone down too deep to remount to his conscious life. Thus, the Faustian theme, found in *The Monk,* exemplifies the "ultimate deepening" of the Gothic dream before which the dreamer, who is Ambrosio or any proscribed hero-villain, must halt. He has arrived at a place with no way out. Adds Professor Levy: "C'est alors que (le reveur) doit, selon Dante, ce magistral reveur de spirales, 'abandonner tout espoir.' "[17]

Professor Levy's inclusion of Dante as *reveur* brings into focus the extensionable fact that *le reveur* can be a visionary like Shelley or Blake, an *artiste* like Mallarme or Poe, a fabulist like Spenser or Orwell, or, with Dante and Bunyan as props, any moralist dealing with interior states within a fictive setting. Thus, without flaw, depravity and salvation—two Dantean themes—can be subjects. The proviso is that the subject not be clinically treated or statistically oriented. Rather, the subject must be humanized, imaginarily set, and include those ups of triumph and downs of tragedy *(verticalites),* or (in Dante's case), the sordidness of depravity and the beatitude of salvation. Obviously, by definition, Dante, a great moralist, is also a great *reveur.* Others: Swift, Eliot, Joyce, Euripides, Browning, and Baudelaire.

Le reveur may be articulate like Eliot or Swift, emerging with a moral plot that is coherent and systematic, yet *onirique* in setting and sign. The condition makes both Eliot and Swift rational dreamers. At the other extreme, *le reveur* may be surreal, leaning on automatic writing, symbolic, associative, vague, yet directional by repetition of motifs. James, Bergson, Freud, and Jung have recognized the manner of communication. Joyce and Woolf illustrate the manner in *Ulysses* and *To the Lighthouse,* respectively.

Le reveur may be a character in a plot as in *Pilgrim's Progress;* or a nation in crisis, as Professor Levy has noted. He ought to be acknowledged as a gestalt psychologist. He will most often be seen as the author—the Dostoyevskan expressionist, the Henry Jamesian impressionist, or the Orwellian satirist (witness *Animal Farm). Le reveur* is then a visionary recording *verticalites.* It follows that, whether rational or surreal, the greatest *reveur* has recorded the best *verticalites* within the most diverse and probable range. Shall we judge

Shakespeare, Dante, Dostoyevsky, or Sophocles as greatest *reveur?* We cannot include didacts like Jesus, Plato, Machiavelli, or Rousseau.

Somewhere between surrealist free-flow and Dantean ordering of the mind occurs the Gothic novel. I would agree with Professor Levy that the Gothic novel is closer to surrealist free-flow than to Dantean order. There is, for instance, a comparable looseness of plot, the automaton character, a leaning on ambiguity and symbol, and an upending of spectacle and action. This aesthetic state encourages one to an awareness of dream-constructs—of interiors too vague and far away to capture, yet too close and meaningful to release. Dante in *La Vita Nuova,* Eliot in *Gerontion,* and Browning in *Andrea del Sarto* approach, but do not enclose, their envisagements to leave them loose for interpretation. Rimbaud's "Bateau Ivre" has a surrealist flow; closer to Gothic is Kafka's "Metamorphosis."

These thoughts, then, underlying or developing from Professor Levy's "Structures Profondes" on surrealism, *le reveur,* and Gothicism.

Because of its dream implications, Gothic architecture seems to Professor Levy to be more related to Gothic literature than is the French Revolution. The distinction expresses Professor Levy's affinity with *"l'axe vertical"* at the expense of *"l'axe horizontal"* in interpreting the English Gothic novel. Levy continues: Burke's treatise on sublimity is an aesthetic recounting of *"l'experience verticale"* found in the Gothic novel. These vertical flights, he adds, are essential to one wishing to know his place in a conceived interior world.

The Gothic novel, says Professor Levy, provides not only different levels of the self *(Le Moi),* but also an ultimate cosmic flight *(L'Axe Cosmique),* proceeding from a descent into "hells" *(Enfers)* to a heavenly ascension *(Ascension).*[18] But the transits condemn the Gothic novel, according to Mircea Eliade—and Professor Levy—as *degradee.* It is the damaged myth-form of an archetype related to Ulysses' wanderings, the Quest of the Holy Grail, and the *roman policier*[19] of criminal-versus-detective.

Especially, however, says Levy, the English Gothic novel manifests a return to one's natal source *(maison natale).* It is a house of absolute intimacy; to the English, it is an ancestral dwelling within which one "descends" into his national past. This national past is not constituted in literal history but in besetting images *(images obsedantes)*—signs in the Gothic novel of a collective myth. The myth, he adds, will not be erudite as in *histoire,* but *"gothique onirique,"* integrating England's national past after, say, 1688 with the events of 1789.

Professor Levy is in sensitive fettle in disclosing that the *Castle of Otranto* followed—not preceded—Walpole's transformation of Strawberry Hill into a Gothic castle. Thus, the constructed towers, battlements, cathedral decor, and staircase not only permitted the Gothic "dream" called *Otranto,* but also concretized a place destined to inspire the accomplishment of automatic writing; to be, then, an *"observatoire du ciel interieur."* [20]

Thus, Professor Levy's underpinnings—*les bases profondes*—of the English Gothic novel. In all, the underpinnings are complex, diverse, and wandering; "French" in temper rather than "German" or "English"; and a presentation of motifs rather than an achieved synthesis. Within that frame, however, Levy's findings have spring and flight, innovation and daring, and, I judge, enough introductory stuff to keep scholars Gothic-minded for decades.

To be sure, "Structures Profondes," in its presentation, does not include the differentiations and value-comparisons that would have been enlightening to us. I shall declare, for instance, at the risk of my head, that Faust's collapse *(La Chute)* and the castle *(chateau, maison, Le Moi)* are more important as symbols in the Gothic novel than the meanings of nature, whether depicted as land, sea, or sky. I shall declare, also, that Freud's symbols, however vital and searching in themselves, are less summative for the Gothic novel than are Jung's myths. Freud's symbols can even take one away from the Gothic plot to set up enclaves of meaning that, however luminous, cast no steady light on the total work. On the other hand, the Jungian pattern, both deeper and broader than Freud's, remains closer to the plot, and can be a parallel and demonstrable fact.

My greater problem, however, in reading "Structures Profondes" is in realizing how far Jung and Freud—and Breton—have taken one from appreciating the Gothic novel as good or bad writing. Always, the aesthetic appreciation must take priority. One must ask, What was lost or gained in effect by my interpretation through Freud or Jung? If enough was lost, a new problem of interpretation has arisen. On the other hand, if the plot had no unity and the language was imprecise, one should ask: What of Freud and Jung—and Breton—was needed to insure my respect for the work? I believe that the English Gothic novel is serious, expresses us, and is mythically plausible. At the same time, I have recognized that no age will exempt the English Gothic novel from structural flaws, excessive action, and dimensionless characterization. I sense that Professor Levy, here and there, has been aware of the latter Gothic problem, but not enough to account the problem as major.

One last complaint. Professor Levy's encompassment of the Gothic novel as dream expression seems to be astoundingly right. But is it dream-literature because conceived in a dream? Or because it reflects *angoisse?* Or because it reveals a continuity and coherence so flawed that the action must "float" since it cannot "run" or "ride"? I believe Professor Levy's position corresponds to the second reason, which is psychological, symbolic, and indeed constructive. For it is saying, "Allow me time and an intelligent reader, and I will make the Gothic novel viable." In contrast, the third reason, an aesthetic jab, is restive and ruinous. It is saying, "Allow me time, good taste, and a practical eye, and I will assure you of the collapse of an inept genre."

I am not pleased to have raised questions about so important a statement as Professor Levy's "Structures Profondes." It represents pre-eminent Gothic scholarship. Levy's references are multi-lingual and major, his insights numerous and profound, and his exploration creative and arresting. My great regret, indeed, is that "Structures Profondes" has not had translation into English. American Gothicists could find it a godsend and a liberation. The English Gothicists, at the least, could find it a replenishment. I have been both liberated and replenished.

Endnotes

[1] Therefore I put Levy's piece at the end of that book, since it constitutes *la grand somme intellectuelle* ("the intellectual sum-up") of *The English Gothic Novel: A Miscellany.* TMH.

[2] Definitions in *Cassell's New French Dictionary: roman,* novel, romance; *conte,* tale; *histoire,* tale, story, narration.

[3] Levy, *Le Roman "Gothique" Anglais, 1764-1824* (Toulouse: Universite de Toulouse, 1968), p. 613. References to *Le Roman* hereafter footnoted as *Levy.* My translation follows.

> Thus, Levy can say: "If the Gothic novel is inhabited by
> a revolution, it is first that of 1688 that affects it." He

adds: "The Revolution of 1688 had been religious as much as political; at the same time that it abolished the last vestiges of manorial despotism, it authorized the definitive rejection of Catholicism and confirmed beyond all excesses the very spirit of the Reformation."

[4] Levy, p. 619.

[5] *Ibid*. From the "age of magic" to the "age of science," and from the "age of poetry to that of the novel."

[6] Literally: "dream-persons" performing "dream-acts."

[7] See Levy, p. 620, f.n. 57. Translation follows: . . . into, then, a dream-world of "gloomy ghosts. . . . nocturnal scenes, funereal universes begotten often by a delirious brain and comparable to incoherent night-dreams."

[8] Levy, p. 622. Literally, "a return to the mother," but related to Freud's regression image, "a return to the womb." The association of house-forms with "a return to the mother" in the Gothic novel is but one of many meanings and contexts connected with that edifice, particularly the castle.

[9] Levy, p. 624.

[10] *Ibid*., pp. 624-626.

[11] *Ibid*., pp. 628-630.

[12] Levy's phrase, p. 639. Literally: . . . "on the level of clear consciousness," . . . .

[13] Levy, pp. 631-634.

[14] Levy, p. 634: . . . "the essential likeness of the dynamic prison." *Essential* here has the connotation of *archetypal.*

[15] Levy, p. 637. The *pittoresque* landscape is not the real one but the verbal or pictorial equivalent, representing only what the artist has seen or wants to see.

[16] Levy, p. 638. "Looking more like an aerial vision than a human dwelling."

[17] Levy, p. 641. "It is then that (the dreamer) ought, according to Dante, that sovereign dreamer of spirals, 'to abandon all hope'." The reference here is to the advice at the entrance to Hell described by Dante in the *Inferno.*

[18] Levy, p. 641.

[19] *Ibid*., p. 642. "The police novel."

[20] Levy, p. 643. "An observatory for the interior firmament." Breton's French, my English. TMH.

159

PART FIVE:

FOLKLORE

CHAPTER TEN

New Light on Pedro Jaramillo

Folklore is commonly defined as a grassroots expression, a lapsed or a submerged culture, or a straw-in-the-wind grasp of daily realities. That it is also an expression of Romanticism should occasion no surprise when one recalls the revival of the folk ballad during the Romantic Age, Herder's interest in folk philosophy and proverbs, Scott's pursuit of Scottish folkways, and Blake's, Wordsworth's and Keats's pick-up of folk characters, myths, and superstitions for some of their finest poetry.

"New Light on Pedro Jaramillo," a long look at a *curandero*, folk doctor, is, then, but another manifestation of a Romanticism that long ago transcended its Age to become a familiar in all kinds of climes and cultures. In this instance, the culture is Hispanic, the clime medical. Then, the setting is South Texas and the person, an illiterate shepherd sprung forth as a man with a *don*, a gift.

In the Romantic lexicon, this introduction comes down to these Romantic facts. Pedro Jaramillo reflects the habits and faculties of the noble savage. More, he has the morality of the common man. He leans on nature for insight and *remedios*, and treats his patients with egalitarian respect. Most of all, he places man's heart over his head and, to cite his special condition, the miracle with its attendant vision over the human act with its attendant common sense.

These Romantic elements and more to be had in "New Light on Pedro Jaramillo." TMH

163

1. Don Pedrito and Romanticism

Don Pedrito is—I cannot emphasize the fact enough—directly in the line of the noble savage made imminent to us all by the Romantics of the late 18th and the early 19th century. He is a medical noble savage, no less, more complex than Chateaubriand's Atala and Wordsworth's leech-gatherer; but not as centered in nature as Rousseau's primitive in the *Discourse on Inequality*.[1]

If a noble savage operating in nature, Don Pedrito is also a transcendentalist operating for God. This fact relates him, however remote in clime and culture, to the earlier Carlyle, the later Coleridge, and that man of the woods and the pond, Henry David Thoreau.[2] Don Pedrito goes to nature for prescriptions as easily as Werther and Faust go for answers.[3] Like both noble savages and transcendentalists, Don Pedrito is attuned to a world that is simple, honest, caring, and good.

Don Pedrito is also a man of dignity and respect. The elements balance and sustain characteristics he shares with Shelley and Blake, a tendency to be visionary and vague.[4] Like the peasant everywhere, his home is the noble savage's, the land. Like many of the transcendentalists—Emerson, Coleridge, and Kant occur to me—he is aware of a divine order and law.[5] These he embroiders into his daily thought and work.

Don Pedrito has unbounded confidence in nature's vegetables, open air, and fresh water.[6] He assumes nature to represent a limitless bounty for his patients. One must recall nature's gift of skip-along joy in the child of nature,[7] of knowledge to Wordsworth,[8] of movement by the daffodils,[9] and of meaning for the Gothic ruin[10] to find in Don Pedrito's *recetas* another illustration of nature's benevolence.

The *recetas* of Don Pedrito fulfill yet startle. He recommends hot water for pimples, tomatoes for hexes, muslin and lard for bug-bite, and baths for delirium and fever. The combination is original—and romantic. One finds its instance in an idiot boy's relaxation before waterfall and moon,[11] in Wordsworth's spin through space from a Highland maiden's song,[12] and in the poet's intimation that what he sees and feels about nature may be implicit in "beauteous evenings" and butterflies, and common to Lucy, Emmeline, and Dorothy.[13]

The instances point to a supernal power called God by Don Pedrito and nature's spirit by a Wordsworth just past thirty. Whatever the name, or parallel, the activity suggests an agent dispensing good will from on high to all below. Belief in such a dispensation is also a romantic characteristic.

Not least, Don Pedrito, like both noble savage and transcendentalist—indeed, like all of the Age except the scientist—recognize Swedenborg's injunction that spirit and matter are separate, with spirit dominant over matter.[14] The conditions allow for morality to become a co-efficient with nature, for the virtues to interlace with the emotions, and for inspiration and vision to be as trusted as trial-and-error experiments. These objectives are the ordinaries of an age Don Pedrito has unconsciously adopted as his own.

Don Pedrito, then, a latter-day romantic? Not too bad an identification of a *curandero* who is apt to be lost in the fuss and fury of regional lore. I believe he belongs to the tradition, especially when I recognize that romanticism is an idea as well as an age, and reflects a kind of temperament and response that, long since, has achieved an indelible state.

But the time has come for you to make your identification of Don Pedrito and of "New Light on Pedro Jaramillo." Both study and man await you just as they awaited me: as uncommon subjects for uncommon hypotheses. Is Don Pedrito more romantic than religious or medieval? No. The romantic identification exists as an after-thought to clarify elements in the man that would otherwise go unexplained. Is Jaramillo less a folk or religious hero than a romantic hero? No. But he exists more clearly as a folk or religious hero if his romantic antecedents are revealed. These first words have tried to do that.

Finally, is "New Light on Pedro Jaramillo" less an objective presentation of folklore than a subjective expression of romanticism? No more questions. They approach insanity. "New Light on Pedro Jaramillo" represents both folklore and romanticism and could not escape its bondage to either identification. But how true that fact is will depend upon your knowledge of the subjects. *C'est tout.* TMH.

NOTES TO THIS SECTION

[1] See Chateaubriand's Atala and Wordsworth's leech-gatherer for examples of literary noble savages; for the *ur*-description of the

noble savage read Rousseau's *Discours sur l'origine et les fondements de l'inegalite parmi les hommes* (Paris: Gallimard, 1965). A translation of the *Discours,* by Roger D. and Judith R. Masters, is available in *The First and Second Discourses* (New York: St. Martin's Press, 1964). Wordsworth's leech-gatherer is, of course, a major subject in the poet's *Resolution and Independence* (1802). Chateaubriand's *Atala* has been translated by Caleb Bingham for the Stanford University Press (1930). Sixty years after its appearance, the definitive study of the noble savage remains Hoxie Neale Fairchild's *The Noble Savage* (New York: Columbia Univ. Press, 1929).

[2] Carlyle's transcendentalism is apparent in his characterization of Teufelsdrockh in *Sartor Resartus* (1833-34). Coleridge's transcendentalism, tentative in *The Rime of the Ancient Mariner* (1798), is definitive in the *Biographia Literaria* (1817) and in his philosophical lectures. For Carlyle's transcendental evidence, the reader should refer either to the Everyman Library edition of *Sartor Resartus* (ed. W.H. Hudson, 1908) or to the Odyssey Press edition (ed. Charles Frederick Harrold, 1937). For Coleridge's, one can refer either to the Nonesuch Press edition, edited by Stephen Potter (1933) or to the Rinehart edition edited by Elizabeth Schneider (1951). Other Coleridge sources: The *Philosophical Lectures* (1949) and *The Inquiring Spirit* (1951), both edited by Kathleen Coburn for Routledge and Kegan Paul, London. A welcome introduction to Thoreau and transcendentalism occurs in *The Portable Thoreau,* edited by Carl Bode (New York: Viking, 1947). Primary sources on the subject include Thoreau's *A Week on the Concord and the Merrimack, Excursions* and "Economy," "Higher Laws," "Winter Visions," and "Conclusion" in *Walden.* A source for the above-mentioned essays: Walter Harding's *The Variorum Walden.* New York: Twayne, 1962.

[3] For two retreats to nature, epochal for their times, see Werther's in Goethe's *Die Leiden des jungen Werthers* (1774) and Faust's in Goethe's *Faust, ein Tragodie* (1790; 1832). Translations of ranging popularity and taste are: *The Sufferings of Young Werther* (tr. Bayard Quincy Morgan. New York: F. Ungar Pub. Co., 1957); and Faust; A Tragedy (tr. Bayard Taylor. New York: Modern Library, 1950), and *Faust, Part I* (tr. C.F. MacIntyre. New York: New Directions, 1957).

[4] Don Pedrito's vagueness lies in his *recetas.* Apparently they work, but, in their simple and ordinary address to the problem, they shouldn't. They represent examples of "cures" originating from

"nowhere"—visionary stuff. As healing visions of the body and spirit, they nevertheless relate to the complex social visions of Shelley and Blake. For Shelley's, read *Queen Mab, Alastor, The Revolt of Islam,* and *Prometheus Unbound;* for Blake's, read *The Marriage of Heaven and Hell, America: A Prophecy, The Books of Urizen* and of *Los* and *The Four Zoas.* In their political and psychological fulfillment, Shelley's and Blake's visions have their own healing power as social *recetas.*

⁵ For Emerson's transcendental thoughtwork, see "The Transcendentalist," "Self Reliance," "Spiritual Laws," "The Over Soul," "Circles," "The Poet," "Nature," "Plato; or the Philosopher," and "Swedenborg; or, The Mystic"—all in *Ralph Waldo Emerson Essays & Lectures.* Edited by Joel Porte (New York: Literary Classics of the United States, 1983). See Kant's *Critique of Pure Reason* and *Critique of Judgment* for parallels that are better organized and reasoned. For Coleridge's transcendentalism, one should wend one's way back to f.n. 2 of this study.

⁶ The reader will find these curative elements of Don Pedrito twice more in this study—necessary, I believe, in view of this study's length.

⁷ For a supply of those young delights ingesting nature with such elan, see Wordsworth's Lucy Poems (1799), *Tintern Abbey* (1798), *The Prelude, I-V* (1805), "We Are Seven" (1798), and "The Emigrant Mother" (1802); also, "Among All Lovely Things My Love Had Been" (1802), "To a Highland Girl" (1803), and "She Was a Phantom of Delight" (1804).

⁸ See Wordsworth's "Expostulation and Reply" (1798).

⁹ See Wordsworth's "I Wandered Lonely as a Cloud" (1804).

¹⁰ See Wordsworth's "Address to Kilchurn Castle, upon Loch Awe" (1803), and *The White Doe of Rylstone* (1807).

¹¹ See Wordsworth's *The Idiot Boy* (1798).

¹² See the poet's "The Solitary Reaper" (1803).

¹³Lucy, Emmeline, and Dorothy—familiars of Wordsworth's earlier nature poems. By 1805, they have ceased to be so prominent in his poetry.

¹⁴ Swedenborg's position on the relationship of spirit and matter is presented by Signe Toksvig in *Emanuel Swedenborg: Scientist and Mystic* (New Haven: Yale Univ. Press, 1948). See especially Toksvig's chapters "Anatomy of Mind and Body," "Anatomy of Soul," "The Great Vision," and "Swedenborg's Clairvoyance."

2. Introduction and Text

Generally, the folk-doctor, of which there are scores, remains a principal in South Texas folk-lore. This study, however, has ignored the scores to concentrate on one, the most famous of South Texas folk-doctors. The study, then, represents, one that only a researchist with intimate access could provide. Lilia Aurora Barrera Cruz, of Rio Grande City and Houston is such a researchist; she has had relatives treated by Don Pedrito, and generations of friends and acquaintances owning Don Pedrito *recetas.*

The largesse is replete: lots of details gained from friendliest offerings. They add a dimension or three to what we know about Don Pedrito, and another layout of his *recetas* to be added to those already on hand.

Ms. Cruz's approach to this Don Pedrito study reflects the assiduousness and the dimensionality she brought to all she did for me in freshman honors English at Pan American University. Not once could I ever ring bells for her writing. Indeed, I would have to put her in writer's purgatory for her repetitions, misusages, and fractured style. But I would have to protect her residence there because of her facts. She has lots of them, and they show up well in this plausible helping of *curanderismo.*

I should say here that Ms. Cruz and I have not made terms on the appearance of "New Light on Pedro Jaramillo" in *Ranges of Romanticism.* She opposes the appearance; I support it. She offers no reason for her stand; I offer every reason I can usher. I believe, for instance, that "New Light on Pedro Jaramillo" intends no harm and is itself knowledge-worthy. I believe also that it clarifies ambiguities surrounding the *curandero* as healer, religious, and romantic. Not least, I am certain that it depicts, as no other study, a *curandero's* growth from man with a *don* to savant with a prayer. Such data is not easy to dismiss. It is not dismissed in "New Light on Pedro Jaramillo."

I should also say that the present draft of "New Light" represents a composite effort of Ms. Cruz and me. The readings, interviews, and first draft are Ms. Cruz's; the title, notes and credits, and final structure and style are mine. We each have entered interpretations into the study; we each have received credit in the notes. Without

Ms. Cruz's research, "New Light on Pedro Jaramillo" could never have been written. Without my rewrite of her report, "New Light" could never have achieved print. Yet, at no time did we commune or correspond on the project. Now, project done, I know that we will not have to.

I should point out that, of the two drafts of "New Light on Pedro Jaramillo," only the latter, the revised draft, is in copyright, and that copyright is in my name. As one might surmise, I am concerned to prevent the revised draft's disappearance or destruction. But I am concerned as well to demonstrate the Bill of Rights' protection of the written word when under duress. With the copyright arrangement, protection has arrived to "New Light on Pedro Jaramillo."

Two last facts and then *finis*. First, I personally assume full responsibility for the appearance of "New Light on Pedro Jaramillo" in *Ranges of Romanticism,* and for its copyrighted state. Second, after the study's appearance in *R of R,* I intend to surrender credit for my contribution to the revised draft to Ms. Cruz. This act will mean to me that she will have become the sole author of both drafts. TMH

Beginneth Ms.Cruz:

Today, fifty-three years after the death of Pedro Jaramillo, much South Texas talk continues about this *curandero's* life and cures. People continue to have faith in him and to add fresh facts about him. Indeed, today, his name may be at its highest peak of reverence and fame.[1]

In *The Healer of Los Olmos,* Ruth Dodson introduces us to Pedro Jaramillo as a *curandero* in Texas. She also tells us how he got his *don,* or supernatural gift, to cure.[2] From Alejandro Ramirez, one of Don Pedro's adopted sons, I have received facts that include Don Pedro's life in Mexico and additional information on how Don Pedro received his *don* to cure. In this study, I would add these facts and others to those collected by Miss Dodson.

Said Alejandro Ramirez: Don Pedrito, as he is called by his believers,[3] was born to Tarascan Indian parents in Guadalajara, Jalisco, Mexico. Already an orphan while yet young, he was taken in by a Mexican family. This family proved to dislike him, treating him less as a foster son than as a servant. To them, he was a shepherd. Don Pedrito often told his dearest friends that he had had a hard life while growing up. He said that, although he was a very young boy, he was expected to do difficult chores. Still, despite the hard life, Don Pedrito refused to leave his foster parents. Said Mr. Ramirez: Don Pedrito remained with them for years beyond his due.[4]

While living as a shepherd with this family, Don Pedrito received his gift to cure. One day, while bringing in lost sheep, he was knocked off his horse by a tree limb. In falling, he landed with his nose against the tree. Unconscious at first, with a terrible nose-bleed, he lay listless for several days. While there, a storm came, then snow. Said Mr. Ramirez: Don Pedrito remembered that, though he had witnessed this bad weather, he had not been affected by it. There had seemed to be a circle around him where no rain or snow had fallen. At length, he had been awakened from his listlessness by a voice which told him that God had given him the gift to heal. The voice said that it was his duty to go practice—in the name of God—his call to help humanity. In that instant, Don Pedrito learned how to treat his nose. To relieve its pain, he went to the pool of water where he daily watered his sheep, and buried his face in it. Said Mr. Ramirez: At the end of three days of this treatment, Don Pedrito was cured.

Miss Dodson mentions that Don Pedrito often told his friends and patients that his nose had remained disfigured so that people would associate his scar with the gift of healing. It was after his nose got well that he decided that he would go out into the world to practice what he considered his call.[5]

Miss Dodson tells us that Don Pedrito came north into Texas in 1881. I found out that, in this year, he was accompanied across the Rio Grande River by a friend, Don Ricardo Gebara. While on this side, reports Miss Dodson, they attended a big feast at the Las Cabras Ranch of Andres Canales (*Dodson 11*). Seeing that the people were nice and needed a doctor, Don Pedrito decided that he would stay and live among them. First, however, he had to return to Mexico on business. In 1883, business completed, he came back to stay in the United States (*Dodson 12*). Don Pedrito established himself at Los Olmos, a ranch one mile north of present-day Falfurrias. I should add that Don Ricardo Gebara built a house at Las Puertas, a ranch five miles north of Rio Grande City.

When Don Pedrito came to South Texas, he was given land at Los Olmos by Julia Garcia Cuellar.[6] Here he built himself a *jacal,* hut, and started to practice his call. Today, people often misunderstand, even malign, the benevolence of Julia G. Cuellar. Some believe

170

that she was Don Pedrito's wife. Some go to the extreme of calling her his mistress *(Olivarez)*. Both statements have been corrected by Don Pedrito's grandson Amador Barrera. Amador explained that *tatita* [sic] *Pedrito,* Grandfather Pedrito, had never married.[7] Amador remembers that his father, Don Severiano, often told him that Don Pedrito was an aware and serious man. Thus, Amadro knows that Don Pedrito understood that having a mistress would mar his reputation.

Later, adds Miss Dodson, Don Pedro Jaramillo was given a plot of land by a prominent rancher of the area, Antonio Hinojosa *(Dodson 14)*. On this land the *curandero* raised many kinds of vegetables for himself and patients. Miss Dodson mentions that he also bought quantities of food in the area store. Don Pedrito made sure that he always had plenty of food for his patients and friends *(Dodson 13, 14)*.

When Don Pedrito first came to Texas, few people knew of his cures. So, he would travel by horse to South Texas towns to treat those afflicted *(Dodson 13)*. Eventually this journeying had to be stopped because of the patients coming to Los Olmos. So many patients were arriving, indeed, that he had to erect tents to house them. Amador Barrera remembers that his father told him that Don Pedrito at the apex of his *curandero* treatments had ten women assisting him at Los Olmos. Often, the good deeds of these women were taken wrongly by people of evil thoughts.

Hearing of his "miraculous" cures, people, after a while, came to see him from all over Texas and beyond. Regardless of ailment or distance, however, no patient received treatment until Don Pedrito knew that the patient had faith in him. Miss Dodson says that he seemed to be clairvoyant *(Dodson, 14)*. If he sensed that an incoming patient had faith in him, he would wait outside his hut to greet the patient. If he sensed that a patient did not believe in him, he, as said, would not treat that patient.[8] Don Pedrito's reasoning on the matter was absolute and invulnerable. Not believing in him meant not believing in God. As he explained to people praising his cures, God was the healing power. His office was to do as God wished.

Don Pedrito's growing name and practice embarrassed the doctors of San Diego, Corpus Christi, and San Antonio, in part because he was sharing with them their patients. These doctors asked the law to look into his methods of healing. They considered him a witch-doctor, invading their hard-earned profession. The law did look into Don Pedrito's practice but only to find that people came to him of

171

their own will. More, the law concluded that Don Pedrito was not competing with the doctors, for he did not charge for his treatments.[9] The doctors, now angry, hit upon another plan to stop the *curandero*. According to one who met Don Pedrito in 1905, the doctors decided upon a banquet, at which they would poison Don Pedrito.[10] They invited Don Pedrito to this banquet and he attended. The first course of the banquet was wine, and Don Pedrito's cup was prepared with a poison formula. When the guests were *brindando,* toasting, all the doctors stared at Don Pedrito, waiting to see him drink the prepared wine. Observing their reaction, Don Pedrito told them, *No temen, que yo no me hago nada. Al contrario pueda que Dios vos castige por sus malas intenciones.*[11] "Do not be afraid. Nothing will happen to me. On the contrary you may get sick because God can punish you for your bad intention" *(Salinas).* All the people at the banquet were astonished at the ability of this man to read minds. The outcome of the banquet was that the doctors got the stomach-ache and ended up asking Don Pedrito for remedies to get rid of it.[12]

Thus, Don Pedrito's practice continued, and, as is well known to the reader of *The Healer of Los Olmos,* he is credited for having cured not only common human diseases, but also animal ailments and witchcraft curses. To the "curings" one can read there, I would add the following which I have picked up.

1. Mrs. Irene Graves Sutherland was treated by Don Pedrito as a young girl. While staying with her brother C. Graves, a railroad agent at Banquete, Irene was much annoyed by the pimples on her face. One day, upon hearing that Don Pedrito had come to Banquete, she decided to ask him for a remedy. When she got to the house where the *curandero* was staying, a woman took her into the room where Don Pedrito sat on a bench. The woman asked Irene to sit beside Don Pedrito. The woman then asked the patient what her trouble was. Irene told her of the horrible pimples. The woman explained Irene's trouble to Don Pedrito, now apparently grown deaf. He prescribed that she drink a cup of hot water each morning for nine mornings. The water was to be scalding, but not boiling.

While Irene was there, she thought to ask for a remedy for a brother who could not sing because of a sore throat. Don Pedrito prescribed that he swallow the raw white of an egg each morning for nine mornings. Both Irene and her brother took their remedies at the same time each of the nine mornings and both recovered completely.

At the same time Irene asked for a remedy for a bunion on her foot. Don Pedrito told her to get some "very fine" olive oil and add to it four or five mashed cloves of garlic. He told her to set the oil where the sun would shine on it for nine days. Afterwards, rub the bunion with the oil. He asked her not to tell anyone what the remedy was, for, if she did, the bunion would return. She followed the prescription given her, and the bunion disappeared.

Later when Irene saw a cousin limping around on account of a bunion on her foot, she felt prevailed upon to share the prescription with her. The result was that the bunion on her cousin's foot was cured but hers came back. In 1960, Mrs. Sutherland still had the bunion.[13]

2. Mrs. Doroteo Perez did not know Don Pedrito, but she recalls the stories her mother has related to her of his cures. She told me one of how Don Pedrito cured her grandmother. Her grandmother Aniseta Bolbora of Roma was very sick. Her sickness continued for several weeks until everyone in the household got worried about it. Brews made from herbs were given to her, and *curanderos* along the Border were consulted, but Mrs. Bolbora did not get well. Her husband decided to take her to Los Olmos to see *el curandero famoso curabe Don Pedrito*. The neighbors tried to discourage Mr. Bolbora from taking his wife, saying that, with her fever, Mrs. Bolbora would not withstand the long journey. Nevertheless, one morning, Mr. Bolbora and several relatives fixed Mrs. Bolbora a cot on the back of a *juayin,* a covered wagon, and set out for Los Olmos. When they got to Los Olmos, Don Pedrito asked them to rest before he prescribed a remedy for the patient. After he saw her, he prescribed a remedy, then sent them back to Roma. As a prescription, he asked the family to have Mrs. Bolbora bathe in a *canoga,* a cattle water-trough, for three days at six o'clock in the morning and to pour water over her body "in the name of God."

At first the family did not want to follow the bathing instructions for fear of speeding her death; but Mrs. Bolbora, amid mumbles, insisted that she had faith in Don Pedrito and was sure that if anything happened to her, it would be God's will. The second day after the lady had bathed in the cold water and had prayed to God for her health to be restored, she showed obvious improvement. She was able to eat a big meal, converse with visitors, and walk without her sister's help to the water-trough to bathe. Though she was a convalescent for several days, people remember that she had gotten rid of her fever and aches by the third day.[14]

This cure of Mrs. Bolbora by Don Pedrito's simple *receta* was the topic of Roma and the surrounding ranches. Soon more people expressed faith in this "benefactor of humanity" and traveled long distances to see him.

3. My aunt, Mrs. Ignacia R. Garza of Falfurrias, was cured by Don Pedrito when she was a baby. At the age of nine months, when beginning to crawl, she was bit by what seemed to be a *cucaracho* [sic].[15] The huge bite on her little leg seemed to affect the bone, then got infected and poisoned her. After trying the only doctor nearby, the mother, discouraged, took her to Don Pedrito. He saw the infection and said that the baby had been bitten by a "poisonous bug." He then gave the mother a *receta*. Said Don Pedrito: Cut fifteen yards of muslin into square pads of one-fourth of a yard each; perform nine washings of cold water, then apply a muslin square of washed lard on the wound. Don Pedrito said that the lard was to be applied three times a week. Mrs. Garza claims that when the muslin square was removed from the wound, the cloth was green in color, and flesh appeared on the cloth. Gradually my aunt was cured, but on her leg remained a huge scar.[16]

4. Jose Maria Ramirez, my uncle, of Hebbronville, Texas, was cured of *susto,* shock, by Don Pedrito in 1904. He had gone into shock as a young boy when he held the hand of a dying man. The man had asked him to hold his hand with one of his hands; with the other, to hold a watch so that he, dying, would see exactly the time of his death. Unfortunately, when the sick man had breathed his last, he threw out his false teeth. My uncle, not knowing that the sick man wore false teeth, went into *susto.*

After this incident, my uncle lost weight and appetite. His body ached and he was unable to work. My grandmother, worried about his condition, called Dr. Solis, a new doctor in Starr County, to come to see him. Still, my uncle's health was not restored. He was then taken to Guerrero, Mexico, to see another doctor, Pablo Trevino. Instead of improving, he seemed to get worse. My grandfather's cousin, Cisto Garcia, heard of my uncle's illness and offered to take him to Falfurrias for a change of environment. Immediately, my grandmother associated the town with Don Pedrito, and asked my uncle to see the *curandero* for a *receta*. My uncle said that he was not about to see that *brujo,* witchdoctor.

When my uncle arrived in Falfurrias, he got worse instead of better. Even pads of hot dirt applied to his aches brought no relief.

Finally, Cisto Garcia decided to take my uncle to Don Pedrito. When he got him to Don Pedrito's house, however, my uncle challenged the *curandero* with a question: *Quiere usted curarme porque mi mama lo quire?* "Would you treat me just because my mother desires you to?" Getting no response, he left in a fit of rage. When he was mounting his horse, Don Pedrito approached to ask that my uncle give his regards to the family. Then he slowly uttered a proverb: *Un clavo saca otro clavo, o si no lo acaba de ramachar.* "One nail helps pull out another; if not, it helps the other nail hold better." My uncle left in a fury.

On his way home to Aqua Nueva Ranch near Hebbronville, he decided to visit relatives in Realitos. When he got there, Lupita and Nacha, his cousins, asked him to take them to the plaza to buy candy. He agreed to go, believing that by going he would calm his anger. But when they got to the plaza, five dogs met them, then chased him. Frightened, he went into deeper shock. Impatient and disgusted, he decided to go straight home. He had had a bad day! When he got home his mother and grandmother asked him for the *curandero's* prescription. He told them that the *brujo* had only given him a meaningless proverb. Upon hearing the proverb, his grandmother explained to him that it meant that his first *susto* would be cured by a second *susto*. Then he remembered that he had received a second shock when the dogs had gone after him. Eventually, my uncle Jose Maria Ramirez recovered completely. He is still alive at 78.[17]

Don Pedrito's fame in Rio Grande City grew as rapidly as it had grown in Roma. Thereafter, almost every day, a "caravan" of people left the town for Los Olmos. When people who could not go heard that someone else was going, they asked him to get *recetas* for them. Thus, when Candelario Laurel and his brother-in-law were going to see the *curandero,* people came to them to request *recetas.* Among them was Don Toribio Lopez, suffering from rheumatism. When they got to Los Olmos, they had only to give Don Pedrito the names of the persons who wanted prescriptions for him to know their ailments and appropriate prescriptions. Unfortunately, however, they neglected to ask Don Pedrito for a *receta* for Don Toribio, and had returned almost to Rio Grande City before remembering they had not. After much worrying over their lapse, Mr. Laurel's brother-in-law said, "Let's just not worry any more. I will prescribe for Don Toribio with a difficult remedy." When they got to Rio Grande City, they distributed Don Pedrito's *recetas;* when they got to Don Toribio, they told him that Don Pedrito had advised him to bathe for three days in cold water at three o'clock in the morning. Sure enough, this remedy helped and Don Toribio was cured. Undoubtedly, his great faith in Don Pedrito helped to perform this cure.[18]

Don Pedrito is known for having healed the bewitched; less known is his refusal to heal a witch. He refused to heal a lady in Premont who practiced black magic on anyone she disliked or envied. Because she could *embrujar,* (bewitch) anyone she wanted to, people were afraid not to be nice to her. One lady, however, was not afraid. Getting information on black magic, she cast a spell that so dominated the Premont lady that her illness was defined as supernatural. Having heard of the wonderful cures effected by Don Pedrito, the Premont lady asked to be taken to him. As soon as Don Pedrito saw the lady, he refused to prescribe for her sickness. Endowed by God with knowing others, he knew at once who this lady was. He said, *No curo a esta mujer porque es mujer de malos procederes. Dios odio lo malo asi es que yo no hago nada incontra de su voluntad.* "I do not treat this lady, because she practices evil. God hates evil, therefore, I will not do anything against His will." This meant that Don Pedrito did not deal with witchdoctors. But he continued to cure people under hex, who had not harmed others (*Perez*).

Because of his stand against black magic, Don Pedrito could cure Miss Herminia Laurel, who had been invaded by evil spirits. Herminia, a beautiful young lady, suddenly seemed to go crazy. After she had been examined by a doctor without results, her parents decided to take her to Don Pedrito. As soon as Don Pedrito saw Herminia in one of her spells, he told her that she had been hexed by someone jealous of her beauty. Then he told her how she had been bewitched. It happened thus: While she was taking a walk on the Plaza in Falfurrias, the person jealous of her beauty had put an egg containing bewitching power down her back. Having the odd feeling of something going down her back, she hit the object, thus breaking the egg. Thinking a spider was crawling on her back, she went into convulsions.

After Don Pedrito had related the happening to Herminia, he told her that it was going to take a long time for her to get well because the egg had been broken. Had the egg not been broken, her ailment would have been cured sooner. He prescribed that she eat plenty of canned tomatoes, at every meal if possible. Eventually, she was cured and her beauty restored (*Laurel*).

As Miss Dodson tells us in *The Healer of Los Olmos,* Don Pedrito even performed cures on animals. Mr. Candelario Laurel had a horse which got an infected hoof after losing its horseshoe. Due to this infection, the horse would not eat. Mr. Laurel's friends kept telling him to shoot the horse to end his sufferings. But this Mr. Laurel would not do because he loved his horse. When Don Pedrito heard of the horse's sickness, he told Mr. Laurel to feed the horse plenty of cold cactus; also, to cut out the mushy part of the cactus, heat it, and apply it to the horse's infection for nine days. Mr. Laurel's horse got well and served him for many more years.[19]

For almost twenty-five years Don Pedro Jaramillo cured the afflicted who came to him. During these years he also became, as said, the foster father of two boys, Severiano Barrera and Alejandro Ramirez. Don Pedrito was asked to adopt Severiano Barrera by Julia Garcia Cuellar, the donor of the land where he lived in Los Olmos. Severiano's mother had died at her childbirth and, because his father had several other small children to feed and clothe, he could not easily take care of the new baby. Hence he gave Severiano to Julia Cuellar. When Julia Cuellar was near death, she asked Don Pedrito to look after her foster son. When she died, Don Pedrito did take Severiano Barrera into his house. He did all he could to please his foster son; he gave him love and things he had not had as a child.[20]

After Don Pedrito had adopted Severiano, many kids would come to Don Pedro's house to play marbles or spin tops with Severiano. Among those who came was Alejandro Ramirez. Alejandro enjoyed being at Don Pedro's house because it was always full of people, so he set about helping with the farm chores. Don Pedrito, seeing Alejandro's desire to help, asked his family to let the boy stay with him. Thus, in 1902, at eight years of age, Alejandro Ramirez came to live with Don Pedrito. He stayed until Don Pedrito's death in 1907.

Don Pedrito was eager to have Severiano and Alejandro educated. First, he taught them to read and write on the basis of the little he knew. But when more people started settling at Los Olmos, and a one-room log-schoolhouse was built, Don Pedrito sent the boys to school. Later, he also sent Severiano to school in Austin, probably to St. Edward's since Don Severiano's wife said the school was Catholic.

Both boys lived with Don Pedrito, but he legally adopted only one, Severiano Barrera. This may help to account for the fact that Alejandro Ramirez gave me unfavorable information about Severiano.

He said that Severiano doubted Don Pedrito's cures and had not appreciated the favors Don Pedrito had shown him. He recalls that when Don Pedrito was close to death, he refused, despite people's request, to give Severiano the power to cure so that he would continue to help humanity.[21] Mr. Ramirez also concurred in a belief shared by others that Severiano never worked a day in his life, and had spent all the money left in unopened letters addressed to Don Pedrito by people rewarding him for his cures.[22]

Compounding these reports is Ruth Dodson's. In response to her request for an interview, Severiano asked for money for the information he would give her. Miss Dodson told about this dun to Judge J. T. Canales, whose mother had been cured by Don Pedrito. Judge Canales' advice to Miss Dodson was that she should not give Don Severiano any credit in her book because he was not worthy of it.[23]

If one would censure Severiano Barrera at this point, it is relevant to know that, in the opinion of Falfurrians, Severiano Barrera was a respectable man, who felt honored to be Don Pedrito's adopted son. Significant as well is the fact that Severiano was permitted to be buried next to Don Pedrito's shrine in Los Olmos, and that his wife remained faithful to him during the period of charges against him. The tone of the Corpus Christi *Caller-Times'* lengthy report of Severiano's death is respectful. It follows:

> Falfurrias—Severiano G. Barrera, Sr., 73, adopted son of South Texas' famed curandero, Don Pedrito Jaramillo, died Tuesday night in a local hospital. Barrera was a lifelong resident of Brooks County.
>
> Miraculous healing powers were attributed to Barrera's foster father. For years before Don Pedrito's death in 1907, hundreds of people came to him each year for cures. Don Pedrito's grave on the old Los Olmos Ranch between Falfurrias and Premont is still decorated with fresh flowers by those who believe in him.
>
> Barrera is survived by his wife Dolores of Falfurrias, five daughters, Mrs. Eva Guerra and Mrs. Dolores Villarreal both of Falfurrias, Mrs. Elida Mora and Mrs. Ninfa Reyes, both of San Antonio, and Mrs. Aurora Harland of Texas City; three sons: Severiano Jr., Amador and Ruben, all of Falfurrias; eleven grandchildren and a greatgrandson.

> Funeral services will be at 4 p.m. Thursday at Sacred
> Heart Catholic Church in Falfurrias with the Rev. Phillip
> Kennedy officiating. Burial will be in Don Pedrito's
> Cemetery at Falfurrias.
>
> Howard-Williams Funeral Home is in charge of
> arrangements.[24]

Finally, in the small four-room home of Mrs. Barrera and son Amador in Falfurrias is a large colored picture of Don Pedrito given to them by Jose Mante Garcia when Mr. Barrera was very sick. On the frame of the picture hangs a black rosary.[25]

The Barrera family remembers that Severiano told them that Don Pedrito asked his son not to bury him until three days after his death. But since the bodies of dead people at that time were not embalmed, it was against the law to keep a dead body without burying it for over twenty-four hours. Thus, Don Pedrito Jaramillo died on July 3, 1907, and was buried next day, July 4. Mrs. Ramona Gonzales, once of Los Olmos but now of Edinburg, was at Don Pedrito's bedside when he died. She remembers that his hand remained warm even after he had been dead for several hours. Today, people wonder what would have happened if he had not been buried. One second-generation believer in Don Pedrito thinks that on the third day after his death, he might have proven his saintliness in some miraculous fashion.

Don Pedro was not excommunicated in his time, nor has he been since, for his ''heretical'' work. It is explained by Falfurrias's older residents that excommunication was unlikely because Falfurrias was only a mission at the time of Don Pedrito's *curandero* practice, and received but occasional visits by the district priest. Recalled as well is the fact that when donations were being gathered for the building of a new Catholic church in Falfurrias, Don Pedrito donated the church bell (*Dodson 60*). This bell is still used by the church in Falfurrias. It probably bears Don Pedrito's name (*A. Barrera*). Finally, this from Amador: Don Pedrito always encouraged his son and Alejandro in the Catholic faith. At a very young age, he taught both boys how to pray with the rosary.

A few years before his death, Don Pedrito gave his patients a letter given to him in 1899. I have translated the letter into English. I have placed a Spanish transcript of the letter in Appendix B. The English translation follows:

Letter from God to His cities, ranches and towns[26]

My sons,

Redeemed by the Holy Cross and by the prayers of My Blessed Mother, I caution you that if it were not for Her, I would have punished your wrong-doings. I ask you to obey thy parents, our Mother, and the church. If you do not do as asked, I will send you hardships which will mangle your hearts so that you will not enjoy anything. If you do not do as I ask, you will soon die, brother against brother. In order to assure your lives, I ask you to do penance and to stay away from scandals. Obey God who gave you life and ask Him for thy protection. Teach your children the Christian religion. Obey thy church and the Images of Saints. Respect your elders. Pray the Holy Rosary of Mary; make penance for thy sins as I ask and My Blessed Mother recommends. Because if you do the contrary, I will cause the earth to open up and swallow you. I will send flames of fire to destroy big cities in the world. This My Mother recommended to Saint Catherine of Siena, St. Theresa of the Child Jesus, St. Domingo of Guzman, St. Francis of Assisy [sic], and the Virgin of San Juan. If it were not for the prayers of My Mother, I would have justified thy doings. Pray the Holy Rosary of Mary and do penance for thy sins. If someone believes that this letter was written by an original man and pays no attention to the Supreme Being through whom everything exists, he will not be worthy of heaven and earth. And he who does as this letter asks and has his family do it too, will be placed at My Right on Judgement Day and they will be forgiven. He who ignores My Letter will not be worthy of heaven or earth and will be given justice. If someone helps the poor, giving charity from his belongings and has no glory, he will get it from me. He who does the opposite will receive a curse. I will send punishments and rare plagues. I will make them unworthy of justice and love. I will send calamities. I will cause man to forget himself. Therefore, I ask you to celebrate Passion Days and do penance. He who keeps this letter without publishing it will be taken care of by Me on Judgement Day and will learn what this letter means. He who is a Christian, copy this letter and he will be placed on My Right on Judgement Day.

This letter was given to a lady dressed in blue, so that she would give it to a bearded man, so that he would give it to St. Paulita. In the name of the Father, the Son, and the Holy Ghost, Amen:

> Transcribed by
> Don Pedro Jaramillo
> March 27, 1899.
> El Paisano, Texas.[27]

This letter is circulated among the relatives of those who got them directly from Don Pedrito. It is thought to contain valuable advice. Today, people believe that the world is full of catastrophes because people have failed to abide by the letter. They believe that wars are fought and people are envious because of God's wrath over their failure to abide. They feel that erupting volcanoes are a sign that soon the world will open up and end in fire. The people who still have a copy of this letter live and pray as the letter says; they ask God's forgiveness for the world's sinners so that the world will not perish.

Mrs. Ramona Gonzales, at Don Pedrito's bedside shortly before his death, says that he discharged nine pink, furry, black-eyed worms from his nose (*Gonzales*). She and her sister received two of these worms. Don Pedrito asked them to keep the live worms for fifteen days without feeding them and then to bury them in the ground. No reason was given for the request. Alejandro Ramirez says that he saw the discharge of the worms from Don Pedrito's nose but does not remember his giving them away. He accounts for this discharge as a sign that Don Pedrito, dying, was leaving this world, but that the worms were staying to keep alive Don Pedrito's miraculous cures (*A. Ramirez*).

It is believed in Falfurrias that the death of Don Pedrito was mourned by people of all ages, Christian creeds, and Latin and Anglo nationalities. Ruth Dodson commented in 1950 on how his reputation had grown since his death (*Dodson 37*). We know as well how accounts of *recetas* to, and healings of, patients extended not only into border states, but also into Mexico. Now, ten years later, his

181

fame has grown even more and the people's faith in him is even more unquestioned.

In 1950, Mr. Daniel Cortez, a spiritualist of San Antonio who uses Don Pedrito's name to cure patients, erected a shrine over Don Pedrito's grave. This shrine, at the Los Olmos family cemetery, is visited daily by people who go to pray for his soul, light votive candles, and put wreaths on his grave. On the walls of this shrine are hung flower wreaths of all kinds, both artificial and fresh. On top of his grave is an aluminum cover where two-day and eight-day votive candles are placed. These candle-holders bear the picture of the Virgin of Guadalupe, the patron saint of Mexico, on one side; and the picture of the Virgin of San Juan de Los Lagos on the other side. When the candles burn out, they are replaced by new ones.

On the day that I visited the tomb of Don Pedrito, forty candles were burning. Inside the shrine were replicas of the Holy Bible Cross, and palm crosses made from palms given out on Palm Sunday. On the tombstone was a small picture engraving of this great faith-healer, with the following words: *Aqui vocen los restos de Pedro Jaramillo, el benefactor de la humanidad. Nacio en Guadalajara, Jalisco, Mexico. Murio en Starr County, Texas el dia 3 de julio de 1907.* "Here lie the remains of Pedro Jaramillo, the benefactor of humanity. He was born in Guadalajara, Jalisco, Mexico. He died in Starr County, Texas on July 3, 1907." At the foot of his grave is an iron rail, or pew, where people kneel to pray to the spirit of Don Pedrito. There is an inscription on the arm-rest of this rail which reads: *Pedro Jaramillo, te hago este presente en recompensa a la proteqcion que de ti recibo. Jose Hernandez 5-1-54.* "Pedro Jaramillo, I make this present to you in recompense for the protection that I receive from you."

On the monument exist not only statues of saints such as Santa Rita, Virgin de San Juan do los Lagos, but also a crucifix and a statue of Jesus. These emblems are Christian evidences. On this monument and on the wall have been left *milagros*—images of ears and legs, for instance, of patients cured through prayer to Don Pedrito. Outside the chapel-like house are benches where people can wait their turn until other people inside the chapel emerge.[28]

Many people leave pictures and letters inside the shrine when they visit to ask for Don Pedrito's protection.[29] Others offer masses for the repose of Don Pedrito's soul. Many families also locate the picture of this phenomenal *curandero* among those of the saints.

Indeed, many have faith in and worship Don Pedrito as though he were a saint. On the other hand, many others do not worship him but pray for him and revere his name.

Three famous spiritualists use Don Pedrito's name to perform cures. These are Don Daniel Cortez of San Antonio; Brother Rey Cavazos, McAllen; and Dona Juanita, La Casita, five miles east of Rio Grande City. To the rear of his home, Brother Rey Cavazos has added a temple dedicated to Don Pedrito's spirit. Dona Juanita in La Casita has set aside a room in her home, where she performs cures with the help of Don Pedrito's spirit. Don Daniel Cortez performed a cure, in that fashion, on Lydia Reyes of Corpus Christi. As a five-year-old, Lydia suffered from "attacks."[30] So, her parents took her to a hospital where the doctors, after many analyses, told the parents that the little girl was sick from a blow she had received on the head while her mother was expecting her. The doctors gave her up as a hopeless case.

Upon hearing of this report, her grandmother persuaded the parents to take the little girl to Don Daniel Cortez. After the family and the little girl were seated at Don Daniel's, he proceeded with hand gestures to call the spirit of Don Pedrito, which he consulted. Mrs. Martinez, also in attendance, remembers hearing Don Pedrito say, *Esta gente ni en la vida ni en la muerte me deja en paz.*[31] "These people neither during my life nor after my death let me rest in peace." Then he told the family that the child's sickness could not be cured by doctors because she had been bewitched by a potion which had been meant to hex her mother, but had cast a spell on the child when she stepped on it. Don Pedrito added that the person who had hexed the little girl intended yet to put a spell on both parents and grandparents. Therefore, it would be wise for them to pray to God for protection through his spirit. This advice scared the grandparents and is the reason they visit often Don Pedrito's grave.

As for the child's *receta,* Don Pedrito asked the parents to stand the child on a new board, then to bathe her with cold running water from the Los Olmos Creek, close to his cemetery. After they did this, the child was cured of the "attacks" but remained dumb.

After five months, they took her back to Don Daniel's spiritual center to consult, once again, Don Pedrito's spirit. This time, Don Pedrito told the parents to take the child to Los Olmos and cleanse her with dirt from his grave. They did so and, after a while, the little girl started to make sounds. Her grandfather told her several words to repeat and finally, upon seeing a cow, she loudly said, *Mira vaca,* "Look, a cow." This was how Lydia Reyes, twelve years old in 1960, was cured by the spirit of Don Pedrito.

Today Don Pedrito herbs are sold on the market by Mr. Fernando Tijerina of Laredo. To use the Don Pedrito trademark, Mr. Tigerina paid Don Severiano Barrera five hundred dollars. Mr. Tijerina has a variety of some thirty-five herbs, which sell for twenty-five cents a box. Mr. Tijerina does not offer a Don Pedrito *receta* with his herbs. They sell, nevertheless; and many people think that these herbs were used by Don Pedrito. Actually Don Pedrito's *remedios* consisted mainly of water, black coffee, and vegetables.

Mr. Jose Mante Garcia, a photographer in Alice, specializes in Don Pedrito's pictures. The pictures have helped Mr. Garcia's studio to become a successful business. Rio Grande City, for instance, is full of Mr. Garcia's Don Pedrito pictures. The pictures consist of two different sittings and a duplicate of one with a prayer on the back. One picture of Don Pedrito—without his hat—is not a real picture of Don Pedrito, according to Amador Barrera. Some people believe, however, that this picture shows Don Pedrito at an older age.

Even though believers consider Don Pedrito a good person, others consider him the opposite. J.T. Canales reported about the latter in a letter to Ruth Dodson. The letter reads:

In the *La Prensa* newspaper published in San Antonio, Texas, was a very scandalous article stating that Don Pedrito was profound in cabalistic literature. It also stated that he was buried in Matamoros, and on every Friday evening, the witches danced over his grave. My mother, always grateful because he cured her of a malignant fever from which she recovered after following the prescription sent by Don Pedrito, read the article and requested me to reply, which I did, and I told the Editor that unless he retracted from such article and published the retraction, I would sue him for damages for libeling the memory of the dead. (*Dodson 22-24*)

The action taken by Mr. J. T. Canales shows how much the people with faith in Don Pedrito's cures approve of him. As said, many people worship Don Pedrito; others pray for his soul's repose. Even devout Roman Catholics, not supposed to believe in *curanderos,* revere Don Pedrito because they believe he was one of God's humble instruments for good among the people.

184

Concluding, I would point out that Don Pedrito's *curandero* practice has become a part of the living history of South Texas, and that his reputation seems only to have begun to grow. More difficult to assess is the role he will play tomorrow: as *receta*-healer with a spiritual voice, or as a spiritual voice using fewer and fewer *recetas*. A project for 2000 A.D. would be to determine what the tendency has become.

APPENDIX A

The following three cures performed by Don Pedrito Jaramillo are representative of the hundreds, perhaps thousands, that he accomplished.

Cure 1

Hermilo Salinas's father-in-law, John R. Everitt, was treated by Don Pedrito. Though Mr. Everitt had heard much about Don Pedrito, he did not believe in him. When he became bedridden from rheumatism, however, and doctor after doctor failed to help him, his wife, who had much faith in the famous faith-healer, induced Mr. Everitt to ask Don Pedrito for a *receta*. Don Pedrito gave Mr. Everitt a simple prescription, as if to dismiss the case, then directed his attention to Mrs. Everitt. He told her that, in the future, God would grant them children who would grow up and move from their ranch to the city. He added that when the children had grown up, they would try to take their mother, who would live longer than their father, to the city. If she went to the city, she was going to have many days of misery, some of joy, and others when she would have little to eat. He advised her to stay at the ranch, where she would always have plenty to eat, even if it were only beans and corn. Here her life would be happy. Today (1960) Mrs. Everitt is ninety-five years old and still lives on the ranch.

Cure 2

Mrs. Sarita Canales of Premont told me of how Don Pedrito had cured her husband Rodolfo, as a young boy, from a molar infection. Her husband had gotten the infection from a crooked molar which had pierced his cheek. The infection caused Mr. Canales to go to bed with much pain and fever. He finally got the molar pulled out by a dentist.

Now, however, though the molar was out, the pain remained. Mr. Canales decided to see Don Pedrito. Don Pedrito, seeing the infection, got a fine piece of glass, washed it in clean cold water and cut the outside of Mr. Canales' cheek. He pressed the cheek and a glob of pus spurted out. Then he told Mr. Canales to massage the operation with cold water for nine mornings. Her husband was cured, said Mrs. Canales, but a large scar remained on his cheek for the rest of his life.[32]

Cure 3

The people of Las Piedritas Ranch had much faith in Don Pedrito. They would come to see him every week and would always bring him some gift. On one occasion, Cesario Garza came along with the Las Piedritas group to see Don Pedrito. It so happened that Cesario's brother, having no faith in this great *curandero,* would mock his *recetas.* When Cesario was mounting his horse, ready to leave, his brother came up to bid him good luck, then said, *Le dicen a ese curandero que me mande una purga.* "Tell that faith-healer to send me a laxative." It had been only about one hour after the group had started their journey when Cesario's brother got a terrible stomach-ache. It was so unbearable that it caused him to remember what he had asked for. Upon seeing that he was getting worse, a friend offered to catch up with the people en route to Los Olmos so they could bring him back a prescription. It so happened that the friend had to go all the way to Los Olmos. When he got there Don Pedrito told the messenger not to worry over the recovery of Cesario's brother; rather, to tell him that his stomach-ache was just a warning not to attract sickness by mocking people. He also told him that all Cesario's brother had to do was to drink, in the name of God, a glass of cold water from a *barrica,* water barrel, and his stomach-ache would be cured. Later, Cesario Garza's brother developed a great faith in Don Pedrito (*A. Ramirez*).

APPENDIX B

I supply a copy in Spanish of the Don Pedrito letter, loaned to me by Alejandro Ramirez.

Carta de Dios (A Sus ciudades, ranchos, y pueblos)

Hijos mios,

Redemidos por La Santa Cruz y por los ruegos de mi Santisima Madre les prevengo que si no fuera por Ella les ubiera consumido vuestras maldades. Les prevengo que veneren a sus padres y a vuestra Madre y la Iglesia. Y si no fuera asi, les mandare penas que despedacen a vuestros corazones para que ni logren cosa alguna. Y si no hacen lo que mando para dentro de poco tiempo moriran unos contra otros y para que aseguren vuestras vidas os encargo que agan penitencia de vuestras culpas y no agan escandalo. Veneren al Senor que les dio la vida y encomiendense a El. Den a vuestros hijos la Santisima religion. Que veneren la Iglesia y Imagenes. Respeten a sus mallores. Resen el Santisimo Rosario de Maria. Agan penitencia de vuestras culpas como yo lo mando y lo recomiendo, yo y mi Santisima Madre. Porque de lo contrario hare que la tierra se habra y se los trage. A todos mandare llamas de fuego que despedasen grandes cuidades del mundo. Asi lo recomienda nuestra Santisima Madre a Catarina de Cena, a Santa Teresa de Jesus, y a Santo Domingo de Guzman, y a Santo Francisco de Assisy, y a la Virgin de San Juan. Y si no fuera por los ruegos de mi Santisima Madre ya les hubiera descargado todo el brazo de mi justicia. Recen el Santisimo Rosario de Maria. Agan penitencia por vuestras culpas. Si alguno creye que esta carta fue hecha por un hombre original y no haga aprecio del Ser Supremo por quien todo existe, sera maldito del cielo y de la tierra y el que ponga esta carta

187

de un punto a otro, el y goda su familia sera el dia del juicio puesto a Mi diestra y les seran perdonados sus pecados. Y el que desprecie esta carta sera maldito del cielo y de la tierra, esprintaran de todo el rigor de Mi Justicia. Si alguno socorre al pobre dandole limosna de sus bienes y no tenga buena gloria, la tendra de mi mano y el que no, maldicion sobre todos sus bienes. Mandare penas y plagas desconocidas. Les hare perder el juicio y todo lo que es amor al mundo. Mandare calamidades que esprimentaran los hombres que se olviden de si mismos. Asi es que guarden los dias de Pacion, agan penitencia. El que tubiera esta carta sin publicar har el cargo el Dia del Juicio y sabra lo que esta carta contiene, y el que fuera Cristiano, copelle esta carta, y sera bendito del cielo y de la tierra, y estara de mi mano. Esta carta fue entregada a una mujer vestida de azul, para que se la entregara a un hombre serado de bazba, para que se la entregara a Santa Paulita. Gloria al Padre, Gloria al Hijo, Gloria al Espirito Santo, Amen:

> Transladada por
> Don Pedro Jaramillo
> Marzo 27, 1899
> en El Paisano, Texas

APPENDIX C

Inside Don Pedrito's shrine at the Los Olmos family cemetery are pictures and letters which people have left. Here are copies of two letters found there. One was written by a lady and the other by a school girl. The letters suggest that people of all ages have faith in this great *curandero*.

Letter 1

Don Pedrito,

    Favor de concederme la salud de mi hija Belen. Os ruego que no sea necesario que entre al hospital. Le ofresco una ofrenda de cinto dolars por ese milagro. Tambien favor de concederme que me hija Perla se componga y halle un buen trabajo.

Paula Garza

Letter 2

Don Pedrito Hermario [sic],

    Please help me in my schoolwork and help me to pass all my exams. Protect me wherever I go. Sir if I pass my exams I promise to bring you my grades and a bouget [sic] of flowers.

    Please help my parents get along with each other and please help us sell the place so we can pay off the house.

    Please help me to meet more friends at school and help me to become popular so that I can become a cheerleader.

    Please help everyone who is sick especially aunt and uncle. Please help me in all this [sic] things and I will always remember you in my prayers.

Thank-you,
Mary Alice Ruiz
San Antonio, Texas

APPENDIX D

South Texas Counties, Cities, and Towns in This Study

I call your attention to the fact that twenty cities and towns and ten counties of South Texas receive mention in Ms. Barrera's study. Together, they enclose South Texas and pinpoint the importance of Don Pedrito as a messenger with cures for the area.

At the center of this sprawl of spots is Los Olmos: ever more ranch than town, and the only South Texas residence of Don Pedrito. Close at hand, performing service to the *curandero* in supplies and transportation is Falfurrias, or, as first called, El Paisano. Ten miles from Falfurrias is Premont, but Premont could be fifty miles away so far as playing a role in preserving the reputation of Don Pedrito.

Removed by fifty-to-sixty miles from Los Olmos are Hebbronville in Jim Hogg County; Realitos, San Diego, and Benavides in Duval; Alice in Jim Wells; and Corpus Christi and Banquete in Nueces. On the periphery of this Don Pedrito world, and removed by as many as 150 miles, are San Antonio in Bexar County; Laredo in Webb; and, closer to the source, Roma, Rio Grande City, and La Casita in Starr County; Edinburg and McAllen in Hidalgo; and Brownsville in Cameron.

In 1988, these places remained crucial centers of Don Pedrito appreciation. TMH

3. Comments

Here ends Lilia Aurora Barrera Cruz's "New Light on Don Pedro Jaramillo." My exegesis will focus on Don Pedrito's traditions, his use of numbers in the *recetas,* and his levels of recognition as a developing *curandero.*

Don Pedrito's Traditions. As said in "Don Pedrito and Romanticism," I find Don Pedrito to represent a continuation of the noble savage tradition—the man of nature identified by Montaigne and perpetuated by Rousseau, Crevecoeur, and Wordsworth.[33] As an Indian shepherd in Mexico, Don Pedrito is the noble savage in essence; as the *curandero* of Los Olmos, he is the medical man at work with nature elements.

I find him also to represent an unofficial Christianity practiced from Christianity's beginnings by those leaning on, but not accepted by, the religion.[34] Don Pedrito's rituals and prayers are Christian; his acknowledgement of God as healer is Christian; and like Jesus and the saints, Don Pedrito is represented as one called by God to do good, to reject evil, and to love Him. Thus, with such a vocation to fulfill in his treatments, Don Pedrito, medical man of nature, becomes also medical man of God. The result is meaningful. Brought into focus is a confluence of religion and nature: of Christianity's rightness and nature's goodness, of prayer's request and nature's supply, and, not least, the conversion of incurable diseases into curable ailments. Such a confluence goes deeply into the Don Pedrito patient. It cancels despair, creates hope, and, as Ms. Cruz has shown, firms up and even transfigures the patient.

A third tradition represented by Don Pedrito lies in his allowing nature to effect its slow cure upon the patient. Don Pedrito's *recetas* impress one as not only simple but safe. As we have seen, they include the use of open air, water, baths, and vegetables. Cleanliness, relaxation, freshness, and diet figure in these nature referents. Set aside is the *curandero's* "drugs," his ointments and teas; emphasized is the "naturalness" of the healing. Allowing nature's slow way to effect a cure may be one reason why Don Pedrito so frequently insisted that a patient allow nine days for a *receta* to do its work. One cannot omit, however, that the procedure may have been his way of using a source for which he had more feeling than understanding.

Considering the traditions inherent in Don Pedrito's *curanderismo,* his function as a liaison between God, nature, and man becomes conspicuous. His role as intermediary puts sense into Don Pedrito's service to believers not so blessed with a *don* as he, but blessed in their preference of him to *medicos* turning out *recetas* for the apothecary to prepare. Lower than God, the Holy family, the angels, and the saints, he was to his patient above not only the professional *medico,* but also all else below that professional. Those below him in status, he treated; those above him gave guidance to him. I guess that, in 1883, Don Pedrito, to his patients, was little more than a *curandero* of good intentions. In 1907, at death, he had become a profound doctor. In 1990, he is, to his believers, an angel of service who heeds God and hears prayers. I, in 1990, am not merely diverted by Don Pedrito's having outwitted South Texas doctors in, say, 1890, who challenged his right to prescribe; nor by his healing of patients whom the conventional doctors could do nothing for. Depend on it: the healer with his eyes on both God and body can better survive in notice, respect, and accomplishment than the healer with his eyes on body. I cite you one who has: Don Pedrito Jaramillo.

Don Pedrito's Receta Numbers. Whether treating himself or others, *three* and *nine* are Don Pedrito's major numbers for his *receta* cabinet. One must keep in mind that his nose was healed in three days; that he wished for his body to remain intact for three days after death; that Don Toribio, though fraudulently prescribed for, was effectively treated for three days at three o'clock in the morning; and that, for her fever, Mrs. Bolbora took baths for three days in a water trough. Others, as one knows, received prescriptions requiring nine days of treatments; and, memorably, nine furry worms emerged from Don Pedrito's nose just before his death. When one associates the fact that nine is reducible to three-squared (3^2), one must conclude that, for Don Pedrito and his patients, *three* had a connection with the Holy Trinity,[35] perhaps the Holy family,[36] and certainly the days of Christ's entombment before his ascension.[37] Such evidence made plausible the prospect that adherence to three days or nine in one's prescription could augment one's cure, and, if need be, assist a miracle.

Here, then, another substantiation of Don Pedrito's claim that his work was God's; and here, once again, more plot-work for proclaiming that Don Pedrito's calling was real and approved from on high. The conclusion could not help but hasten Don Pedrito's becoming a legend while yet alive.

Don Pedrito's Levels of Recognition. Anyone's effort to tie down Don Pedrito will end up finding him complex. As a healer, he is a *curandero* fashioning remedies; as a man of God, he is an answerer of prayers and a maker of miracles. The range, great enough from the one to the other, involves, at the least, seeing Don Pedrito first as an illiterate man with a *don*, then as healer and moralist;[38] thereafter as judge with a voice, then as benefactor, legend, and possible saint.[39] I suggest that these imprints, 1881-1907, may be contained in six levels of recognition, but know that such a containment may constitute a restriction. We yet know too little about the beloved doctor's beginnings in Mexico or in South Texas; and his confirmation as a true man of God remains in the balance.[40] Worse, if one considers the work needed to be done, the real research on Don Pedrito—since he became a legend—may have begun too late. What has emerged is a blend of both legend and man, with distinctions too vague to separate the one from the other.[41] I must ask, therefore, that the reader regard what's to follow as a mere effort to supply order where there has been none. He may be more than will be depicted here. I shall only protest that what he seems to be here is grounded in fact rather than in fantasy.

To me, the first imprint of Don Pedrito, after his beginnings as shepherd, must be that of apprentice-healer using his lore with vegetables and herbs, but with little notion of his *don* other than that he had one.[42] I recognize at this stage a *curandero* illiterate but shrewd, and intuitive to the point of clairvoyance. Fortunately, his shrewdness is balanced by his sympathy for the sick, but his intuition is weighed down by his inexperience. On this level, his feeling for *recetas* become what they are to remain, generalities rather than specifics; and his kindness and tolerance are shortened by his lack of interpretation. At this stage, Don Pedrito seems only a level or two above those champions of speculation, the horologist and the numerologist. Moreover, in his inexperience, his *curanderismo* is crowded with solutions from inspiration rather than from knowledge. Most crucial, whatever his age,[43] in the beginning his sensations and emotions, less in thrall to his *don,* had to vie with his moral judgment for dominance.[44]

To be sure, Don Pedrito as *curandero* was never to remain on an apprentice-level of practice. He achieved a second level in which the moralist in him filtered into the practical man, and the decent man that he was gained precedent over his faculties. We know from Ms. Cruz that Don Pedrito did take a stand in facing off both the *bruja* of Premont and the area doctors challenging his treatment of the sick. The two encounters tell us that Don Pedrito was brave, did not fluster when challenged, and, as a healer, was humble and honest before God. Not least, at this stage, his sense of service—his obligation to heal the sick—seems absolute. I suggest to you that Don Pedrito's journeyings into South Texas for patients stopped when his character became so uppermost in his treatments that his patients found a visit to Los Olmos a compulsive heal-fest. Don Pedrito had become an indispensable agent of good health and right action.

One can assume that, on this second level of development, Don Pedrito had become a successful *curandero*. Remaining at this level, however, would not have made him either memorable or saved from obloquy. I would compare his state to that of the family doctors whose diagnoses may be right or wrong, but whose beneficence is real and compelling.

Don Pedrito was no more to remain on this second level than on the first. One notes in the limited evidence at hand an intensification of character that begins to overwhelm the simplicity of his *recetas.* Enhancing this impression is a sovereignty over his patients and a relaxation before both the ploys and gibes of his detractors. There seems to be a sense of justice operating in treatments that had excited merely his tolerance, and his service to man ties in more and more as a service for God.[45] He transmits his religiousness to his adopted sons.[46] Where he had been vaguely generous, he is now firmly good; and where the man in him remains evident in dispensing *recetas,* the angel in him appears in his willingness to receive, to accept, and to understand. At this level, the third, Don Pedrito is transcending his service as *curandero* to become a servant of God. I suggest that this level has become firm by the time of Don Pedrito's adoption of Alejandro Ramirez, 1902. Don Pedrito will have five more years to live.

At level four, compassion seems increasingly a prominent element in Don Pedrito's healings. Not tolerance or generosity, not patience or bravery, and surely not justice which can be stern or goodness which can grow soft. Rather, all these elements rarefied into the one that, in Christianity, transcends all others. Don Pedrito, healer, has become to his world a benefactor of mankind. Though the *recetas* remain simple, the patients' belief in their *curandero* is more rapt. His *recetas* become ultimate remedies. His practice grows and his reputation spreads. Trains from the North and wagons from the South bring the halt and the sick to Falfurrias. At Los Olmos, his attendants defend him against mendacious talk. Don Pedrito, in his way, has become the *curandero* ideal, the essence of a man with special advice. The level is preliminary to that on which Don Pedrito rests today. The summit represents a summation worthy of any man's career.

The summit, level five, is the affirmation that Don Pedrito has become legend. It was achieved no later than 1904 and perhaps earlier.[47] Now, in 1990, eighty-three years after his death, he is a healer of hearts as well as of bodies; his remedies are emblems of truth, and his service to man outsize in reputation. Once an illiterate with a calling to cure, this simple man has become an object of reverence and a source for requests. A benefactor turned hero,[48] he has evolved into a candidate for sainthood.

This high office of God, sainthood, would call for another level of appreciation of Don Pedrito which I, a scholar, can not make. I would say, nevertheless, that to be a saint is more than to be hero, healer, moralist, judge, or compassionate man. It is, indeed, to be these imprints with the added quotient of a love intense enough to transform another's life.

I offer these explanations of Don Pedrito in 1990 as, alas, a guess-work of signs rather than as a facsimile of his life. I am not certain of the time-span in his development as *curandero*. I cannot pinpoint all the pivotal experiences of his life. I have to rely too much on parallels of development—from innocence and youth to awareness and adulthood—that is in us all rather than special to him. Above all, I have not documented enough of Don Pedrito's development from *curandero* with a call to spiritual advisor with a confirmation.

Still, the levels provide a pattern of growth from earlier to later, and, perhaps as important, both identify and explain the daily changes of temperament and attitude that could characterize him to the end. For Don Pedrito, like any other exceptional man with, say, too little sleep and too much burden, could, in a day's duty, range up and down the above levels while treating his patients. I am saying, then, that Don Pedrito could misprescribe, then correct his diagnosis; be carpish toward, then declare for, a patient; or be apathetic in prayer, then reverent. Still, after such allowances for being mortal and human, one fact remains dominant: Don Pedrito seems to have had success in his work from the beginning. Today, that beginner's success may constitute first proof of what, in 1990, remains in the balance: that Don Pedrito Jaramillo, *curandero* and liegeman of God, 1881-1907, ought to become at least an ''unofficial'' candidate for the spiritual office he has not yet received. TMH

NOTES TO THIS SECTION

[1] For modern evidence of Pedro Jaramillo's achievement of ''reverence and fame,'' see below Lilia Aurora Cruz's description of his shrine in 1960; also, in footnote 28, my description of his shrine in 1988. TMH

[2] *To cure.* An English verbal fixed in the vocabulary of the Hispanic South Texan. A less ambiguous word than *to cure* in English is *to heal. To cure,* however, has the association of the Hispanic's

curar (Sp.), to cure, to give it a momentum that *to heal* does not have. Still, perhaps no real problem exists in its use. *To cure* can mean *to heal* without chatter if one dismisses the fact that *curing* can also refer to what one does to hams, bacon, sausage, dried fruits, cement, and herbs. This dismissal may be automatic to the Hispanic when referring to a Don Pedrito "curing." TMH

³ *Don Pedrito.* This diminutive of *Don Pedro* has best described the *curandero* since the 1880's. The diminutive will be used here as a way of honoring his continuing presence among his believers. Mind you, physically Don Pedrito was small, even tiny. But that association with his name has been secondary for too many decades to be meaningful to one discussing Don Pedrito today. TMH

⁴ Interview. Mr. Alejandro Ramirez, Falfurrias, Texas. Hereafter cited in the text as *A. Ramirez.* LAC. *An addendum:* The researchist Lilia Aurora Cruz has adopted in this study a respectful *Mr.* and *Mrs.* in addressing Hispanic adults—these instead of *Senor* and *Senora,* or, in the English manner, with no mention of title in one's first reference to a person, and with only the last name mentioned in subsequent references. I have respected Ms. Cruz's preference of address while finding the convention an elaboration of no real consequence to the study. TMH

⁵ Ruth Dodson, "The Healer of Los Olmos," in *The Healer of Los Olmos and Other Mexican Lore.* Edited by Wilson M. Hudson. Dallas: Southern Methodist Univ. Press (1951), p. 11. Hereafter cited in the text as *Dodson.* Miss Dodson's account of Don Pedrito remains the fullest and most extensively researched of any to date.

⁶ Reported by Mrs. Romula Olivarez, a distant cousin of Julia Garcia Cuellar. Hereafter cited in the text as *Olivarez.*

⁷ Interview. Mr. Amador Barrera, son of the *curandero's* adopted son Severiano Barrera. Hereafter cited in the text as *A. Barrera.*

⁸ Reported by Mrs. Ramona Gonzales, who met Don Pedrito in 1905. Hereafter cited in the text as *Gonzales.*

⁹ The money Don Pedrito received for his treatments represented voluntary offerings by his patients. As God's agent, Don Pedrito could not charge for healings he felt to have been wrought by God. Yet, if the patients elected to leave with him a gift, he could accept it as patrimony left in his care for God. Legally, the doctors had no way of circumventing this kind of "sacred" plan. TMH

¹⁰ Reported by Mr. Hermilo Salinas, my [Mrs. Cruz's] distant

uncle. Hereafter cited in the text as *Salinas.*

[11] Throughout this study, one will find Don Pedrito's Spanish to lack the punctuation devices typifying that written language. I have allowed this omission of punctuation to remain since unable to consult with Ms. Cruz on the problem. It is likely that Don Pedrito had an illiterate's knowledge of spoken Spanish which, when transferred to written Spanish, would read as written here. I should add here that translations from Spanish to English, unless otherwise noted, are Ms. Cruz's. TMH

[12] Today (1960), one questions the naivete of the doctors in attempting to poison Don Pedrito, or in asking for a *remedio* from the *curandero* for a stomach-ache given them, as the story goes, for their misdeed. The story is too "dramatic," perhaps, even, too moralistic. It does not record what doctors, an educated group, would do; rather, what an innocent, uneducated folk would believe, or want, them to do. Nevertheless, the story is accepted as true by most of my interviewees, and it may be. LAC paraphrased by TMH.

[13] The first of three unpublished cases recorded by Ruth Dodson, but given to me for publication.

[14] Interview. Mrs. Doroteo Perez, granddaughter of a patient cured by Don Pedrito. Hereafter cited in the text as *Perez.* LAC. Addendum: *Curaba, juayin,* and *canoga* are not listed in *Cassell's Spanish Dictionary.* I suggest that Ms. Cruz's usage represent coinages characteristic of Border Spanish encountered along the Rio Grande River. TMH

[15] *Cucaracho* [sic]. *Cassell's Spanish Dictionary* lists *cucaracha,* cockroach, as a feminine-ending noun. TMH

[16] Don Pedrito's *receta* for Mrs. Garza is complex and atypical. I tried making an anomaly out of that fact to Ms. Cruz while she was yet Ms. Barrera, but to no avail. Her aunt's account had become the "family" account, and the family's legacy to the Don Pedrito world of *recetas* for bug-bite. TMH

[17] Interview. Mrs. Eloisa Garcia. Jose Maria's sister. LAC. Addendum 1: Mr. Garcia was 78 in 1960. TMH. Addendum 2: Mr. Garcia's story represents another instance of how Don Pedrito's reputation got a boost in his time. First, a patient tries a doctor of "scientific" medicine without results. Then, the patient, upon the advice of an older, wiser person, goes, after misgivings, to see Don Pedrito. Within a spate of time plus a collation of nature's simples—with, perhaps, a touch of *susto,*—Don Pedrito effects a change of

health. Another cure by Don Pedrito is ready for the records, and his plaudits can again be told. TMH

I am impressed with the romnticism implicit in this procedure. Don Pedrito turns to nature for his *receta* elements, and nature, lover of man, supplies them. Thus, an intimate rhythm of life between nature and man has been set, plus this romanticist law: The closer to nature lives man, the more will he receive her benefit. For Don Pedrito, the benevolence of God, healer, remains ascendant in this arrangement, but one can assume that many cases of *susto, mal de ojo,* and *empacho* occurred in which God's help, while at hand, was not as immediately sought as nature's. TMH

[18] Interview. Mr. Candelario Laurel, a friend of Don Pedrito's. Hereafter cited in the text as *Laurel.* LAC. Addendum: This account of Don Pedrito's healing prowess in Rio Grande City contains a passel of references to *recetas,* prescriptions, and *remedios.* The mixture is typical in Hispanic talk in South Texas. Whereas, in the Anglo world, a prescription is not necessarily a remedy, in the Latino world a *receta* is presumed to be a *remedio.* This imprecise connection may illustrate a vulnerability of both folk-language and folk-healing. Perhaps the vulnerability could be waived in the case of Don Pedrito healings, for I cannot recall a report in which Don Pedrito *recetas* did not become *remedios.* But none of the other *curanderos* were up to Don Pedrito in resources for effecting a "cure." Thus, in the lapse of the *curanderos* in defining the difference between *receta* and *remedio,* and in the lapse of their patients in seeing the difference, lies a prediction of what will be: a yielding of the *curandero's* simple prescriptions, with God in the balance, to the more material, but more precise and convincing, prescriptions of the pharmacist and the *medico.* TMH

[19] There can hardly be an end to the cures the people of South Texas can credit to Don Pedrito. For three more healings in this study, see Appendix A.

[20] Interview. Mrs. Severiano Barrera, widow of Don Pedrito's foster son. Hereafter cited in the text as *Mrs. S. Barrera.*

[21] Don Pedrito explained to the people making the request that Severiano must receive his own call, that God's gift to cure was a supernatural—non-human—power. The people, of course, had thought otherwise since Severiano—and Alejandro—wrote Don Pedrito's prescriptions for him. They overlooked the fact that Don Pedrito had told Severiano what to write. Severiano helped because he, better

schooled, knew better than Don Pedrito how to write.

[22] *Don Pedrito's money.* Amador Barrera seemed positive that his father, Don Severiano, had inherited at least $25,000.00 from his foster father, including, one assumes, the monies in unopened letters to him.

[23] Fact taken from a letter from Judge J. T. Canales to Miss Ruth Dodson. Date of letter, unknown.

[24] This newspaper clipping was shown to Mrs. Cruz by Mrs. Severiano Barrera. The obituary appeared in the *Caller-Times,* December 17, 1959, on page 16 of Section C. TMH

[25] The day of Mr. Garcia's gift to the Barreras is in Severiano's favor. It is All Soul's Day, November 2, 1959. TMH

[26] Owner of the letter, Alejandro Ramirez. LAC. *Addendum.* Both English and Spanish translations of "Letter from God to His cities, ranches, and towns" presume the existence of an *ur*-text of this letter in God's translatable language. The precise *ur*-text, of course, is not available except as a phenomenon of inspiration or empathy by the receiver of the message. I could insist that the *ur*-text of the letter is Spanish since the letter's recipient was Hispanic, and that all other texts are but translations of the Spanish text. I shall not. Such insistence would challenge an innocence about communication and a will to believe in miracles that the letter needs, whatever my cynicism about its origination. TMH

[27] *El Paisano.* El Paisano (Falfurrias) was in Starr County in 1899 rather than in Brooks. Los Olmos Ranch, at the time, was considered to be in El Paisano.

[28] One has only to visit Don Pedrito's shrine to behold further growth in his reputation. The lighted votive candles have doubled in number, the wreaths, tripled, and the letters, cards, and *milagros* are too numerous to count. A wing has been added to the shrine; more graves have been added to the cemetery; and, most significant, a building for Don Pedrito candles and literature has been erected. One could put aside this building with the comment that Don Pedrito has become "good business" to his Falfurrias supporters. Much more relevant to the truth, however, is the fact that Don Pedrito continues to escalate in prominence and acceptance. This fact may even be phenomenal. TMH

[29] See Appendix C for two of the letters found in Don Pedrito's shrine.

[30] *Attacks.* A vague medical description for which I have no

precise identification. In Spanish, the equivalent is *ataques*.

[31] Interview. Mrs. Antonio Martinez, grandmother of Lydia Reyes.

[32] Interview. Mrs. Sarita Canales, Premont. Last note by LAC; remaining notes by TMH.

[33] See "Of Cannibals" in *Montaigne's Essays and Selected Writings* for, perhaps, the inaugural celebration of the noble savage. *MESW* is a bilingual edition, translated and edited by Donald M. Frame (New York: St. Martin's Press, 1963). For an 18th-cCentury depiction of noble savage as American Farmer, see St. John De Crevecoeur's *Sketches of Eighteenth Century America* (Edited by Henri L. Bourdin, Ralph H. Gabriel and Stanley T. Williams. New Haven: Yale Univ. Press, 1925). Rousseau's characterization of the noble savage in the *Discours sur Inegalite* is definitive and, more than Montaigne and Crevecoeur, set the conditions of its survival into the nineteenth century. Helping along were Wordsworth's turn-of-the-century man of the soil to be found in "Simon Lee" (1798), *Michael* (1800), and *Resolution and Independence* (1802).

[34] Heresies vivid in the history of Christianity: Gnosticism during Primitive Christianity; Arianism during 4th-century Christianity; in the 5th century, Nestorianism and Manichaeism; and during the Middle Ages, Waldensianism, Manichaeism, Catharism, Averroism, Albigensianism, and all phases of the "magic arts," including sorcery and witchcraft. To the hostile or apathetic observer, Don Pedrito's work can represent at worse demonism and witchcraft, at best magical healing. Both have been given short shrift by the Catholic Church. (For a fuller discussion of heresies, see Jeffrey Burton Russell, *A History of Medieval Christianity Prophecy and Order.* New York: Crowell, 1968; A.S. Turbeville, *Mediaeval Heresy and the Inquisition.* New York: Dutton, 1921; and "Magical Healing" in *Inquisition and Society in Early Modern Europe.* Edited and translated by Stephen Haliczer. London: Croom Helm, 1987, pp. 88-144.)

[35] The Holy Trinity: the Father, the Son, and the Holy Ghost.

[36] The Holy family: Mary, Joseph, and Jesus.

[37] Christ was three days in the tomb before his resurrection.

[38] The successful *curandero* must receive his call from God to heal; his ability to heal is proof that he has the call. To have the call, however, and to hold it, the *curandero* must be regarded as good rather than bad and able to distinguish right from wrong. In this sense, the

curandero becomes a moralist, acting on his patient with *recetas* on the one hand, and with prayers and injunctions on the other. I believe that the latter outweighs the former in healing importance, which is to say that in every *curandero* lies the gravity of the moralist. In Don Pedrito's case, this gravity of the moralist became the sovereignty of the judge in his appraisal of *brujos,* gossipers, liars, and atheists.

[39] *From healer to moralist to judge to benefactor, legend, and saint.* The progression is orderly; the images develop in seriousness and scope to reveal the ultimate purpose of the true *curandero:* to do good for God. I would contest the definition of the *curandero* in *Cassell's Spanish Dictionary* as a "quack" or a "witchdoctor." Those engaged in *curanderismo* reserve such epithets for those practicing out of ignorance, deceit, or malignity; not for those practicing out of ignorance, perhaps, but with some faith in God's support for their vocation.

[40] *True man of God and possible saint.* I hear that the Catholic community of Falfurrias has petitioned Rome for Don Pedrito's sainthood. I have not secured a substantiation of this report.

[41] *Legend and man.* I suspect that Don Pedrito's account of the injury of his nose and his subsequent call is real, but the account of his protection from snow and storm while he lay helpless is myth become legend. Again, his *recetas,* his treatment for *susto,* and his confrontations with doubters are real, but the "nine furry worms" emerging out of his nose, his voice from the dead, and his letter from God seem like more myth become legend. Who knows in 1990? And what difference would it make to a believer? To him, Don Pedrito has transcended both legend and reality to become an embodiment affecting lives.

[42] Guess-work, here. No one has recounted Don Pedrito's early years beyond historical facts of what happened. I assume that Don Pedrito, being of mortal flesh, had more of the frailties to which flesh is heir as a younger person than as an older one with more experience and knowledge. Thus, what I have said would depict a *curandero* when his awareness was tentative, experimental, perhaps faulty—in fact, like that of almost anyone else, but with a difference.

[43] *Don Pedrito's age.* Astonishingly, no one in South Texas knows the curandero's age, nor have the records in the Guadalajara area been examined. This fact confirms the problem implicit in beginning too late the life and career of a legendary man. Since his is legend, who cares about his age? Age is less an identification than

his success as a doctor and a social force.

[44] More guess-work, but germane as a statement about an awakened younger person with a call. The younger he was, the more he was subject to intuition and impetuousness. These elements would mar his moral judgment and *receta* accuracy.

[45] *Justice of healing.* A vague phrase unless seen to connote the rightness of healing, therefore the naturalness of good health. To see healing as a moral prerogative is not an insanity; the opinion underlies the Pythagorean Oath and has been the virtue as well as the pride of doctors, whether *medicos* or *curanderos.*

[46] *Don Pedrito's religiousness.* Before becoming a *curandero* in South Texas, Don Pedrito had been a Catholic in Mexico. His religious training in Mexico became a part of his sons' religious training in South Texas.

[47] At best, more guess-work, with an allowance of five years as one's margin for error. Don Pedrito's enthusiasts have shown him no favor in not recording by the year the Don Pedrito events they so freely discuss. His legendary status may have already begun by the time he ceased his journeyings to patients and began to receive them in Los Olmos. Still, there is no positive proof that this is so.

[48] Sketchiest of treatments in this study has been Don Pedrito's status as a romantic hero. He is less romantic hero than folk or religious hero, but one cannot ignore the idolatry of Don Pedrito by his constituents, his identification with the common folk, his reliance on nature for herbs, and his adoption of a life in nature as shepherd and healer.

WORKS CITED

Dobie, J. Frank, ed. *Tone the Bell Easy.* Austin, Texas Folklore Society, 1932.

Dodson, Ruth. "The Healer of Los Olmos" in *The Healer of Los Olmos and Other Mexican Lore.* Ed. by Wilson M. Hudson. Dallas: Southern Methodist Univ. Press, 1951.

Barrera, Mr. Amador, foster son of Severiano Barrera, Falfurrias.

Barrera, Mrs. Severiano, wife of Severiano Barrera, foster son of Don Pedrito, Falfurrias.

Canales, Mrs. Sarita, Premont.

Dodson, Miss Ruth, Corpus Christi.

Garcia, Mrs. Eloisa, my aunt, Falfurrias.

Garza, Mrs. Ignacia, my aunt, Falfurrias.

Gonzales, Mrs. Ramona, an aged woman who met Don Pedrito in 1905, Edinburg.

Laurel, Mr. Candelario, a friend of Don Pedrito's, Rio Grande City.

Olivarez, Mrs., Romula, Rio Grande City.

Perez, Mrs. Dorotheo, Premont.

Ramirez, Mr. Alejandro, one of Don Pedrito's adopted sons, Falfurrias.

Salinas, Mr. Hermilo, my distant uncle, Benavides.